THE
Literate
Puzzler

Rita Norr & Audrey Tumbarello

Sterling Publishing Co., Inc.
New York

Edited by Jeanette Green

Library of Congress Cataloging-in-Publication Data

Norr, Rita [date]
    The literate puzzler / by Rita Norr & Audrey Tumbarello.
      p.   cm.
    Includes index.
    ISBN 0-8069-0706-1
    1. Word games. I. Tumbarello, Audrey [date]. II. Title.
GV1507.W8N62   1994
793.73—dc20   94-19668
                                       CIP

3 5 7 9 10 8 6 4 2

Published by Sterling Publishing Company, Inc.
387 Park Avenue South, New York, N.Y. 10016
© 1994 by Rita Norr & Audrey Tumbarello
Distributed in Canada by Sterling Publishing
℅ Canadian Manda Group, One Atlantic Avenue, Suite 105
Toronto, Ontario, Canada M6K 3E7
Distributed in Great Britain and Europe by Cassell PLC
Villiers House, 41/47 Strand, London WC2N 5JE, England
Distributed in Australia by Capricorn Link (Australia) Pty Ltd.
P.O. Box 6651, Baulkham Hills, Business Centre, NSW 2153, Australia
Manufactured in the United States of America
All rights reserved

Sterling ISBN 0-8069-0706-1

• Contents •

Acknowledgments

Thanks to our families for tolerating missed meals and frenzied schedules. To our agent, Elizabeth Knappman, our gratitude for continued confidence and support. Particular thanks to Ann Dietz for her expertise in puns and anagrams. Also, our appreciation to our friends in the Scrabble community, especially the Park Slope Scrabblettes and Ann Sanfedele. And to Jeanette Green, our editor at Sterling, thanks for diligent attention to detail, which gave us our "traveling shoes."

• Word Structure •

"X" Marks the Spot

Use the whimsical and punny definitions below to find these words which contain the letter "X" plunk in the middle.

1. Physical attribute of some women __ __ X __ __

2. A mister who repairs things __ __ X - __ __

3. Lots of guts __ __ X __ __

4. Louis or shorts __ __ X __ __

5. Called the Lone Star __ __ X __ __

6. Tinkerbell, for one __ __ X __ __

7. Chemically, two of O __ __ __ X __ __ __

8. Literary don __ __ __ X __ __ __

9. Not very clear __ __ __ X __ __ __

10. People acting in place of others __ __ __ X __ __ __

11. Some political leaders __ __ __ X __ __ __ or __ __ __ X __ __ __ __

12. Not exactly authoritative __ __ __ __ X __ __ __ __

13. Some blondes __ __ __ __ X __ __ __ __

14. Highly disagreeable __ __ __ __ X __ __ __ __

15. Phone-o-grams __ __ X __ __

16. Homely homily __ __ X __ __

17. Blender job __ __ X - __ __

Split Ends

Add one letter to the beginning and one letter to the end of these words to make another ordinary word. Do *not* use an "S" in the beginning or end.

Example: A M U L E T

1. __ R E S T __
2. __ A X E S __
3. __ B O A R __
4. __ O T I C __
5. __ H O R A L __
6. __ U R E A __
7. __ A L E E __
8. __ A M E N __
9. __ P I N E __
10. __ O V E R T __
11. __ H O R N __
12. __ L O W E R __
13. __ P L A N __
14. __ R U G A __
15. __ I M I D E __

16. __ I L I A __
17. __ H E A P __
18. __ U N D E __
19. __ A B R I __
20. __ U N D O __
21. __ H I D __
22. __ R Y A __
23. __ M O N __
24. __ Y E N __
25. __ V A T __
26. __ U R B __
27. __ A C T __
28. __ B A T __
29. __ E L S __
30. __ F I R __

Split Ends II

Add one letter to the beginning and one letter to the end of these words to make another ordinary word. Do *not* use an "S" in the beginning or end.

Example: <u>C</u> L I N G <u>Y</u>

1. __ R E E D __

2. __ R A V E R __

3. __ I D E S __

4. __ E U R O __

5. __ W O K E __

6. __ Q U A T E __

7. __ W H I R __

8. __ E N O W __

9. __ H A N G __

10. __ O N U S __

11. __ I S B A __

12. __ R O Q U E __

13. __ V I L L __

14. __ I M P I __

15. __ R A T I O __

16. __ R A G I __

17. __ L E A S __

18. __ N O P E __

19. __ I N I A __

20. __ I N T E R __

21. __ P A R __

22. __ M O T __

23. __ E G G __

24. __ V I E __

25. __ I R K __

26. __ A D S __

27. __ P I S __

28. __ J I N __

29. __ O L D __

30. __ E L D __

Split Ends III

Add one letter to the beginning and one letter to the end of these words to make another ordinary word. Do *not* use an "S" in the beginning or end.

Example: R̲ A D O N̲

1. __ P R O __
2. __ N O W __
3. __ V A R __
4. __ X I S __
5. __ D I E __
6. __ H I P __
7. __ M U S __
8. __ I L K __
9. __ L O B __
10. __ W I S __
11. __ J U G __
12. __ W A S __
13. __ K I N __
14. __ U R N __
15. __ N A W __

16. __ I N S __
17. __ H E M __
18. __ L A X __
19. __ G I N __
20. __ C U T __
21. __ H O S E __
22. __ E A S T __
23. __ A C R O S S __
24. __ H E S T __
25. __ L I M A __
26. __ A T T I C __
27. __ D U C A T __
28. __ L E A R __
29. __ I N D I E S __
30. __ R A N K __

Split Ends Plus I

In this variation of Split Ends, add one letter to the beginning and one letter to the end of these words to make another ordinary word. You *may* use an "S" in the beginning or the end, provided that the "S" does not make the word plural.

Example: S̲ C U L L E R Y̲

1. __ H I E S __

2. __ K I D D O __

3. __ E X P O __

4. __ O G L E S __

5. __ C R A W __

6. __ T A L K I E __

7. __ L O B B E R __

8. __ R A L E S __

9. __ C R E W __

10. __ T I N G L E S __

11. __ C R I B __

12. __ C A M P __

13. __ P A R E S __

14. __ M A R T __

15. __ E X I N E S __

16. __ H E A T __

17. __ H I V E __

18. __ T A R D O __

19. __ A U N T I E __

20. __ H A R P __

21. __ T H Y __

22. __ A F A R __

23. __ L A Y __

24. __ N I P __

25. __ A L I E N __

26. __ C U M M I N __

27. __ L A M I N G __

28. __ C O W __

29. __ H E C K L E S __

30. __ C H I N E S __

Expansion Joint

Keeping the letter sequence given, insert one letter in each word below to change it into another word. You may not add the letter to the beginning or to the end of the word.

Example: chorine, chlorine

1. BODIES

2. IMPERIL

3. ROUND

4. FALSE

5. MOODY

6. GENTLE

7. CORNEAL

8. MONEYED

9. HABITAT

10. HIDEOUS

11. IMPUDENT

12. BESIDE

13. PAYDAY

14. CURIOS

15. BELTED

16. MOUSE

17. TURKEY

18. EXCEPT

19. GOAD

20. MORALITY

21. BLUSTER

22. COSHED

23. WATERED

24. EXPIATION

25. DEPRECATE

26. CONTINENT

27. NUTRIENT

28. INSOLENT

29. ANTIRUST

30. FRESHEN

Whodunit

Become a word sleuth. Take one set of letters from the first column (A–Q) and add it to the beginning of a word in the second column (1–17) to form a new word.

Example: S T I N + G R A Y = Stingray

A.	B A R S	1.	__ A R T Y
B.	B O R O	2.	__ B L U E
C.	C A R A	3.	__ D I C E
D.	C R O S	4.	__ I L L Y
E.	E A R P	5.	__ L U G S
F.	G H E T	6.	__ O U R S
G.	H A R B	7.	__ O O Z E
H.	J A U N	8.	__ R A I D
I.	M A H A	9.	__ R A J A
J.	N O N P	10.	__ S W A Y
K.	P R I N	11.	__ T O E D
L.	S C H M	12.	__ T O O L
M.	S H R E	13.	__ T O U T
N.	T R U E	14.	__ U G H S
O.	U N A F	15.	__ U N I T
P.	W E E V	16.	__ V A N S
Q.	W H O D	17.	__ W I S H

Whodunit II

Become a word sleuth. Take one set of letters from the first column (A–Q) and add it to the beginning of a word in the second column (1–17) to form a new word.

Example: S T I N + G R A Y = Stingray

A.	A L P H	1.	__ A B E T
B.	A N T I	2.	__ B A N G
C.	B L A S	3.	__ C A P E
D.	D O O R	4.	__ C E E S
E.	E P I S	5.	__ E R G S
F.	F I A N	6.	__ E W E R
G.	I C E B	7.	__ F O R E
H.	I N H U	8.	__ J A M B
I.	L O C K	9.	__ J A W S
J.	P A S T	10.	__ M A L E
K.	P I N A	11.	__ M A N E
L.	Q U A G	12.	__ M I R E
M.	R E V I	13.	__ O D E S
N.	S C R U	14.	__ R A M I
O.	S E A S	15.	__ T E A R
P.	W H E A	16.	__ T I N Y
Q.	W H I Z	17.	__ T O F F

Whodunit III

Become a word sleuth. Take one set of letters from the first column (A–Q) and add it to the beginning of a word in the second (1–17) column to form a new word.

Example: S T I N + G R A Y = Stingray

A. B E N E	1. __ A I R Y
B. C R O S	2. __ A B Y E
C. D O M I	3. __ B I K E
D. F L Y S	4. __ B O N D
E. M I N I	5. __ C A R T
F. N O N D	6. __ F I S T
G. N O S E	7. __ F I T S
H. P A C I	8. __ G A Y S
I. P E I G	9. __ H A W K
J. P U S H	10. __ L A C S
K. R O C K	11. __ N O E S
L. S A N D	12. __ N O I R
M. S H E L	13. __ P E C K
N. T H E O	14. __ R E M S
O. T O M A	15. __ S C U T
P. T R U S	16. __ T E E D
Q. V A G A	17. __ W I C H

Whodunit IV

Become a word sleuth. Take one set of letters from the first column (A–Q) and add it to the beginning of a word in the second column (1–17) to form a new word.

Example: S T I N + G R A Y = Stingray

A.	A R M C	1. __ A Z O N
B.	D I S O	2. __ B A I T
C.	E M B L	3. __ B E Y S
D.	E N S C	4. __ D O F F
E.	J A I L	5. __ E R N E
F.	M O N O	6. __ G A Z E
G.	O U T B	7. __ H A I R
H.	P L A S	8. __ H I R E
I.	R E A T	9. __ H O P S
J.	S A L I	10. __ L A Z E
K.	S A P P	11. __ N I T S
L.	S A U T	12. __ O N C E
M.	S T A N	13. __ P I A N
N.	S T A R	14. __ P O L Y
O.	S U B U	15. __ T A C H
P.	T E A S	16. __ T I C S
Q.	T H E S	17. __ V A R Y

Whodunit V

Become a word sleuth. Take one set of letters from the first column (A–Q) and add it to the beginning of a word in the second column (1–17) to form a new word.

Example: S T I N + G R A Y = Stingray

A. A L B A   1. __ A I D S

B. A S T E   2. __ A I R S

C. B A R M   3. __ B I E R

D. C H A P   4. __ B U T S

E. C O C H   5. __ C O M A

F. C O U S   6. __ C O R E

G. D R U G   7. __ D U A L

H. F L A B   8. __ D I T S

I. F R O S   9. __ G I S T

J. G L A U   10. __ H E R O

K. H A L I   11. __ I N L Y

L. L O V E   12. __ K E Y S

M. P L A U   13. __ L A I N

N. R A N C   14. __ L I L Y

O. R E S I   15. __ M O R E

P. S Y C A   16. __ R I S K

Q. W H I S   17. __ T E D S

Expand each four- or five-letter word below by adding all the given letters to the front and back to form another word. The original word must remain unchanged within the newly formed word.

Example: T H E N + A C I T U = a u T H E N t i c
            M I T T + C E E M O = c o m M I T T e e

1. P O L E + A N N O = _____

2. D O M E + E O R T = _____

3. R O S E + E E K N = _____

4. A C H E + B L O R = _____

5. H A N G + A H I S = _____

6. K N O T + A B E N = _____

7. R I N G + E E M U = _____

8. R A F F + G I I T = _____

9. P A R T + A D E H I = _____

10. I N S E T + A I O P T = _____

11. T I N E + A I R R Y = _____

12. T E R M + A D I M N S = _____

13. T E N + I L S U = _____

14. S I L O + E N P = _____

15. R I O T + A C I P T = _____

eYESight II

Expand each four- or five-letter word by adding all the given letters to the front and back to form another word. The original word must remain unchanged within the newly formed word.

Example: F E T E + A A C I R = c a FETE r i a
             R A T E + G S T Y = s t R A T E g y

 1. M I E N + I O P T =   _____

 2. R E I N + E H O T =   _____

 3. R O S E + C E P T U =   _____

 4. B R A N + E E M M =   _____

 5. H A N G + A C E L R =   _____

 6. P A G A N + A D O P R =   _____

 7. L O V E + A C E F L R =   _____

 8. T I L E + O S T T =   _____

 9. Q U I T + M O O S =   _____

10. F O R T + C E M O R =   _____

11. R O M P + I M P T U =   _____

12. T E R M + A A F H T =   _____

13. T I C + C I I M R S =   _____

14. S P A R + A A G S U =   _____

15. C O H O + A C I L L =   _____

Expand each four- or five-letter word by adding all the given letters to the front and back to form another word. The original word must remain unchanged within the newly formed word.

Example: R E A D + I L L M T = t R E A D m i l l
            M I N I + C E E R S = r e M I N I s c e

1. C H I N + E I S S T =   _____

2. C H E S T + A O R R =   _____

3. H A L E + A D M R S =   _____

4. S E N T + D E R Y Y =   _____

5. P A S T + A I N O T =   _____

6. L I O N + H I L M T =   _____

7. R A P E + A P S T =   _____

8. L O C K + A B D E =   _____

9. H A R M + A C P Y =   _____

10. H A I R + A C M N =   _____

11. C R I B + A E S S =   _____

12. L A T E + A P U =   _____

13. T H Y + A E M S T =   _____

14. R O W + B E I N S =   _____

15. U S E + B H O O Y =   _____

Expand each three- or four-letter word below by adding all the given letters to the front and back to form another word. The original word must remain unchanged within the newly formed word.

Example: R E A D + O O R T = t o R E A D o r
            L E S T + A C E I L = c e L E S T i a l

1. N O W + I S S U T = _____

2. C A R + A I M N O = _____

3. A R M + A C E K R = _____

4. O W N + A B D E T = _____

5. R U D E + I M N P T = _____

6. T H I N + I K M S = _____

7. P O T + E I M N S = _____

8. N U T + E I M S T = _____

9. F I G + G H N T U = _____

10. P O L O + G O T Y = _____

11. N I N E + I S S T = _____

12. H E R + E O P R S U = _____

13. L I E N + C E E L T = _____

14. B L E W + A A E R T = _____

15. S T A B + E L N U = _____

Expert eYESight
Only for those with extremely keen vision!

Expand each word below by adding all the given letters to the front and back to form another word. The original word must remain unchanged within the newly formed word.

Example:

M E M O + A C E M O R T = com M E M O rate
A-L I S T + C I I R T U = ritu A L I S T ic

1. S C O N C E + I I M N O P T = _____

2. T I C + A E I L P P R = _____

3. U N D E R + A C H L P T = _____

4. T I M E + C E E N R T = _____

5. A N T I + C E E L R V = _____

6. S E W + E F H I O U = _____

7. D E N S + A C E N O T = _____

8. H Y D R A + A B C E O R T = _____

9. B A R D + B E I M O R = _____

10. P O S T + A E H O P R = _____

11. L I F E + A E O P R R T = _____

12. THEMATIC + A A I M N = _____

• Puns & Anagrams •

Joyce Shtick—Hospital

Hidden within each sentence below is a word or phrase relating to a hospital. Cryptic crossword puzzle fans may already be familiar with the types of word play used—anagrams, homophones, puns, and hidden words. To get you started, the first answer is *ambulance*, an anagram of the words *male Cuban*. The number of letters for the answer is in parentheses.

1. The confused patient transported in the emergency vehicle is a male Cuban. (9)

2. I see you are getting very special care in the hospital. (3)

3. Sir, grey is the color of the standard operating gown. (7)

4. Well, I want something un-grey, especially when I'm on that stretcher. (6)

5. The doctor-in-training will see each of you in turn. (6)

6. A "D," miss? I only give service in the entering area a "D" rating. (9)

7. Ray's room is right after section W. (4) (4)

8. May I rent this crib until I can buy one? (9)

9. Gene, mercy! Call the nurse immediately! (9)

10. I can sue, R.N.; so, you'd better have proper coverage. (9)

Joyce Shtick—Paris

Hidden within each sentence below is a word or phrase relating to Paris. Cryptic crossword puzzle fans may already be familiar with the types of word play used—anagrams, homophones, puns, and hidden words. To get you started, the first answer is *Seine*, a homophone of *sane*. The number of letters for the answer is in parentheses.

1. It is not sane, I hear, cruising in a *bateau-mouche!* (5)

2. When walking down this boulevard, try the cheesy samples some of the cafés offer. (6) (7)

3. Travel royally, the layout is worth the small amount of confusion. (4)

4. The velour drapes were not suited to the art display. (3) (6)

5. If you have time for it, leisure strolls through the gardens are romantic. (9)

6. Having time trouble? It can be the quickest route! (5)

7. The stained-glass windows are not red. A meander down the aisle will reveal glorious colors. (5) (4)

8. So, animal lover, smile! (4) (4)

9. At noon, leap on the tour bus and learn about this great Frenchman. (8)

10. When the trip is over, sail less, enjoy fabulous sights. (10)

11. The tour guide's name was, strangely, Quartarius. (5) (7)

Joyce Shtick—High School

Hidden within each sentence below is a word relating to a high school. Cryptic crossword puzzle fans may already be familiar with the types of word play used—anagrams, homophones, puns, and hidden words. To get you started, the first answer is *computer*, sit*com put Er*ica. The number of letters for the answer is in parentheses.

1. In acting class, a sitcom put Erica at the keyboard. (8)

2. Two bewildered Maxes took the biology finals. (5)

3. Jim thinks one must be athletic to be a well-rounded student. (3)

4. Subtract the "D" and that confounded subject is gradable. (7)

5. She confusedly trimmed her nails before taking the typing test. (7)

6. Arthur would rather use a brush than a ballpoint. (3)

7. Shakespeare did well in this and mistakenly thought he should hang out his shingle. (7)

8. A knowledge of wingspan is helpful when studying physics in Madrid. (7)

9. Unclear sign on blackboard: "SNs teaming to do the task." (10)

10. Likely to catch a cheater! (7)

11. "C" in your name? Register in row three if this is your last year. (6)

12. Sachem is trying to learn the periodic table. (9)

Joyce Shtick—Visiting the Zoo

Hidden within each sentence below is a word relating to zoo inhabitants. Cryptic crossword puzzle fans may already be familiar with the types of word play used—anagrams, homophones, puns, and hidden words. The number of letters for the answer is in parentheses.

1. Did you see the baby bird trapped in the towel? (5)

2. I don't think a raptor describes that kind of bird. (6)

3. A very agile muralist must have painted the arboreal mammal on the ceiling of the main entry hall. (5)

4. Did your aunt elope and take that African trip? (8)

5. Does Veronica R. want to meet me by the meat eater? (9)

6. Is that bird's plumage really flaming orange? (8)

7. Why is Kay sneaking up on that viper? (9)

8. Has Pa ten of those feathers from the game bird? (8)

9. The wading bird's foreleg retains that color of feathers into adulthood. (5)

10. That mammal complains loudly if put in a bare cage. (4)

11. This reptile is a real maniac! (6)

12. That animal eats too slowly when given the rootiest plants. (8)

13. Before strolling to the other habitat, let's see the deer. (6)

Joyce Shtick—Joy of Foods

Hidden within each sentence below is a word relating to foods or food preparation. Cryptic crossword puzzle fans may already be familiar with the types of word play used—anagrams, homophones, puns, and hidden words. The number of letters for the answer is in parentheses.

1. Didn't Rose marry the herb gardener? (8)

2. This crustacean treat will bolster your spirits. (7)

3. There wasn't a soul in the seafood restaurant. (4)

4. Ha! Novices eat their pizza plain. They're wrong! (9)

5. You must stay in the room to stir and thicken the sauce. (7)

6. Don't have the crab alone; serve it with another shell-fish. (7)

7. Don't order your sandwich from that deli; it does deliver worst! (10)

8. Following this diet regimen, you must avoid certain lemon pies. (8)

9. Pairs of these with cottage cheese are good low-calorie lunches. (5)

10. Take Mary's word, fish *is* brain food. (9)

11. A bear hug! Mr. Tangled gave me one at the barbecue. (9)

12. We can catch up on news while eating our fries. (7)

13. Even though the vegetables are assembled with art, I choke on large pieces of this one. (9)

Joyce Shtick—A Day at the Office

Hidden within each sentence below is a word relating to a day at work in an office. Cryptic crossword puzzle fans may already be familiar with the types of word play used—anagrams, homophones, puns, and hidden words. The number of letters for the answer is in parentheses.

1. Did Pat mention P. Jenkins was interviewing her at 4 P.M.? (11)

2. Is that the right coiffe for a white-collar job? (11)

3. If they were organized, the crystal factory wouldn't be so messy. Stemware here, there, and everywhere! (6)

4. It's a cinch; add 50 and you'll do this to the deal! (6)

5. She predates the use of Lotus 123 at this office! (11)

6. To be practical, end around the last day of each month. (8)

7. They're like the gestapo, watching every stamp I use! (7)

8. Without a fax machine, are you keeping your board of directors informed? (8)

9. The typewriter works well except for the "S," which sticks when you turn it on. (6)

10. She counted 1,000 pieces of paper as evidence for that case. (8)

11. That's right! Some authors do this better than others! (5)

Word Doodles & Alphacryptics

About Word Doodles

These visual puns use symbols, placement, size, shape, and style to convey various words or concepts. They can represent phrases, sayings, titles, names, places, and so forth. Here are some examples.

1,0010,000	ARIZONA (arranged diagonally)	PAID I'M WORKED
one in a million	*Raising Arizona*	I'm overworked and underpaid.

Cooking Class

Decipher these word doodles which represent kitchen and menu items. *Bon appétit!*

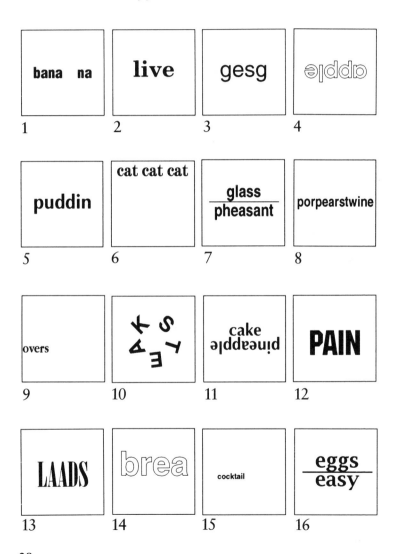

1. bana na
2. live
3. gesg
4. apple *(upside down)*
5. puddin
6. cat cat cat
7. glass / pheasant
8. porpearstwine
9. overs
10. STEAK *(letters scattered)*
11. cake pineapple *(upside down)*
12. PAIN
13. LAADS
14. brea
15. cocktail
16. eggs / easy

28

Songs & Musical Compositions

Decipher these word doodles which represent the names of well-known songs and musical compositions.

1. STAND ME

2. MY WINGS / WIND

3. SYMPHO

4. noel noel noel noel noel noel (repeated)

5. TU∕LOL∕PS

6. THEUBORNSA

7. MOON / SONATA

8. GOLDEN GATE / TWSERA

9. HOPES

T.V. Time

Decipher these word doodles which represent popular television shows. Most are American shows.

1.

HOUSE

PRAIRIE

2.

**RAH!
OLÉ!
BRAVO!**

3. SUCCESSWEALTHLOVEGOODLUCKHAPPINESSHEALTH

4.
oursoursoursoursours
oursoursoursoursours
oursoursoursoursours
oursoursoursoursours
oursoursoursoursours
oursoursoursoursours
oursoursoursoursours
oursoursoursoursours
oursoursoursoursours
oursoursours

5. STAIRS

6.
**POTATO
CHOCOLATE
WOOD**

7. NIGHTNIGHTNIGHTNIGHT

8. *Murder*

9. PRICE

People

Decipher these word doodles which represent the names of famous people.

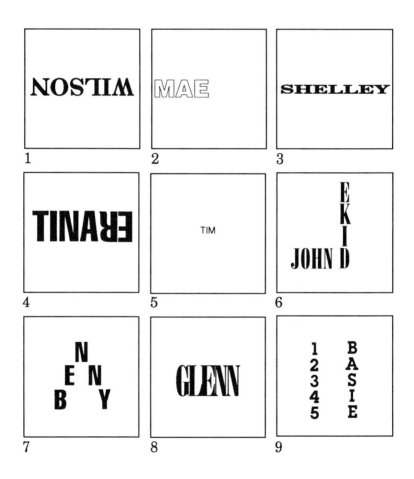

1. NOSTIW

2. MAE

3. SHELLEY

4. TINARE

5. TIM

6. JOHN D / EKID

7. N E N B Y

8. GLENN

9. 1 2 3 4 5 / BASIE

Matinee

Decipher these word doodles which represent famous American movies.

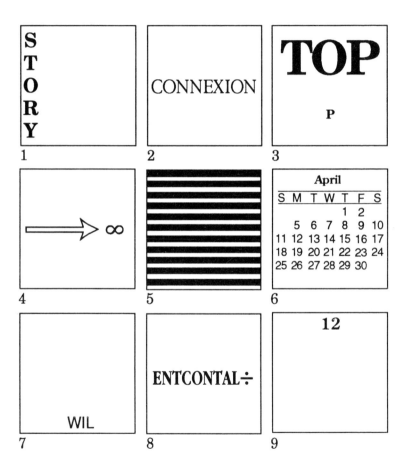

Matinee II

Decipher these word doodles which represent famous American movies.

1

2

3

4

5

6

7

8

9

Decipher these word doodles which represent famous American movies.

1.
JOHN WAYNE
JIMMY CARTER
KEVIN COSTNER
and
MAGGIE SIMPSON

2.
DEATH
&
TAXES

3.
3:14 PM, 4:21 PM

4.
CIRCUI

5.
TA   BLES

6.
PAGANINI
ROOF

7.
ON OR
ABOUT
JUNE 22

8.
ALL
ALLALLALL
ALLALLEVEALLALL
ALLALLALL
ALL

9.

Book Club

Decipher these word doodles which represent titles of famous works. We've given you the authors' names to help you; match the rebus with the author and title.

1. MINISTER

2. THE SO_{RC}EW

3. HICANS

4. ABCDFGHJKLM NOPQRSUVWYZ

5. CATCH, CATCH

6. WOMA

7. HENRY HENRY HENRY HENRY

8. ASTRANGERSTRANGELAND

9. PASSAGE

Joseph Heller, Kenneth Roberts, James M. Barrie, Henry James, Jean-Paul Sartre, William Shakespeare, Lillian Hellman, Robert Heinlein, James Fenimore Cooper

Book Club II

Decipher these word doodles which represent titles of famous works. We've given you the authors' names to help you; match the rebus with the author and title.

Arthur Rimbaud, William Styron, Charles Dickens, Alexander Pope, John Braine, Chinua Achebe, John Steinbeck, James Baldwin, John Buchan

Book Club III

Decipher these word doodles which represent titles of famous works. We've given you the authors' names to help you; match the rebus with the author and title.

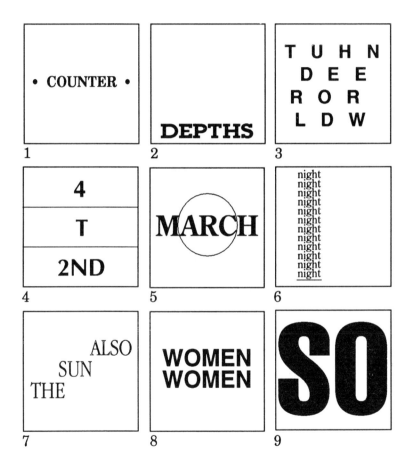

• COUNTER •	DEPTHS	T U H N D E E R O R L D W
1	2	3
4 T 2ND	M(ARC)H	night (×13)
4	5	6
ALSO SUN THE	WOMEN WOMEN	SO
7	8	9

John Dos Passos, Aldous Huxley, William Shakespeare, Alberto Moravia, Ernest Hemingway, Edna Ferber, Maxim Gorky, Fyodor Dostoevski, George Eliot

Decipher these word doodles which represent titles of famous works. We've given you the authors' names to help you; match the rebus with the author and title.

Ivan Turgenev, Booth Tarkington, George Orwell, George Bernard Shaw, Katherine Anne Porter, Joseph Conrad, Henry James, William Shakespeare, Jean Anouilh

Alphacryptics

Look carefully to see if you can determine the word or phrase suggested by the alphabet strings below. Confused? The first answer is *nohow* (no H, O, or W); #2 is *fatback* or *finback* (F at back). You're on your own!

1. A B C D E F G I J K L M N P Q R S T U V X Y Z

2. A B C D E G H I J K L M N O P Q R S T U V W X Y Z F

3. A B C D F G H I J K L M N Q S T U V W X Y Z

4. A B C D E F G H I K L M N P Q R S T U V W X Z

5. A B C D **E** F G H **I** J K **L** M N O P Q R S T U V W X Y Z

6. Ⓐ A B C D E F G H I J K L M N O P Q R S T U V W X Y Z

7. A B C D E F G H I √ J K L M N √ O √ P √ Q R S T √ U V W X Y Z

8. A B C D E F H J L P Q R T U V W X Y Z

9. A Ⓑ C D E F G H Ⓘ J K L M Ⓝ Ⓞ P Q Ⓡ S T U V W X Y Z

10. A B C D E F G H I J K L M N o p Q R S T U V W x Y Z

Alphacryptics II

Look carefully to see if you can determine the word or phrase suggested by these alphabet strings.

1. E E O R S T

2. A B C D E F G H I J K L M N O P Q R S T U V W X
   Y Z   A D Y

3. A B C D F G H J K L N O P Q R U V W X Y Z E I
   M S T ←

4. a B C D E F G H I J K L m n o P Q R S T U V w X Y
   Z

5. B A C D F E S H L J N K G M O P Q R T U V I S W
   X Y Z

6. A B B C D E F G H I J K L M N O P Q R S T U V W
   X Y Z

7. Ⓐ BⒸⒹⒺ F G H I J K L M Ⓝ O P Q R S T U V W
   X Y Z

8. C H O P R A B D E F G I J K L M N Q S T U V W X
   Y Z

9. A B C D D E F G H I J K L M N O P Q R S T T U U
   V W X Y Y Z

10. E O R V A B C D F G H I J K L M N P Q S T U W X
    Y Z

• Word Meaning •

Double Identities

Many people's names are also acceptable ordinary words or terms. Below are the definitions of the first and last names of famous people. Test your vocabulary and discover who they are.

Example: irregular plural of term describing dark, flat areas of moon; lilies described breathlessly by Hepburn <u>Maria</u> <u>Callas</u>

1. policeman's club; fine glassware
   _____ _____

2. pungent root often used as a spice; plural of radio term indicating message received
   _____ _____

3. hereditary unit; more primitive or unrestrained
   _____ _____

4. long, thick nail often used on railroads; shelter from the wind _____ _____

5. male cat; skeins of yarn _____ _____

6. mollusk-made gem; male deer
   _____ _____

7. honey; babbling streams _____ _____

8. a drugged drink; shelf above fireplace
   _____ _____

Double Identities II

Many people's names are also acceptable ordinary words or terms. Below are the definitions of the first and last names of famous people. Test your vocabulary and discover who they are.

Example: to hunt or chase; to pursue in order to capture or overtake   <u>Chevy</u> <u>Chase</u>

1. a sleeveless hospital gown; ready money in currency or coin _____ _____

2. holiday evergreen with red berries; one who pursues game for food or sport _____ _____

3. college official responsible for enforcing rules; bird, usually preceded by *purple* or *house*

    _____ _____

4. baby kangaroo; chesspiece which moves diagonally

    _____ _____

5. aesthetically meaningful rearrangement of materials; one who works in a carnival

    _____ _____

6. to droop or become limp; official who manages a nobleman's household _____ _____

7. informal name for a cat; bright green color

    _____ _____

8. seemingly effortless charm; smooth or slippery, often said of ice _____ _____

9. solidified animal or vegetable oils; a black-and-white-spotted game piece _____ _____

Double Identities III

Many people's names are also acceptable ordinary words or terms. Below are the definitions of the first and last names of famous people. Test your vocabulary and discover who they are.

Example: to raise with a lever, often a car; a champion (British dialect) <u>Jack</u> <u>Kemp</u>

1. deep red precious stone; the letter "D"
   _____ _____

2. to issue forth from a defensive position; a cultivated expanse of land _____ _____

3. to slowly come to an end, dwindle; wolf-like North American carnivorous mammal
   _____ _____

4. a type of blackbird; worn and exhausted appearance, gaunt _____ _____

5. one who wins the spoils; having reached full growth or development _____ _____

6. one who leaves a gratuity for a waiter; to pierce with a horn _____ _____

7. Scotch for *soul* or *mettle*; a bull's very loud cry
   _____ _____

8. slang for amphetamine tablet; archaic for master of the household (used in Salem)
   _____ _____

9. from French, a male sweetheart; structures erected over waterways _____ _____

Equivokes

Determine the proper definition for these words.

1. NIGHTJAR
   a. a type of chamber pot
   b. any of a genus of bird related to the whippoorwill
   c. a container for cleansing cream

2. SKYHOOK
   a. a hook conceived as being suspended from the sky
   b. a showy flying maneuver
   c. an astronomical configuration

3. LONGHEAD
   a. a highbrow
   b. a long-skulled person
   c. an avid fan of classical music

4. HELLBOX
   a. a derisive name for television used by theatre owners
   b. a backstage waiting area for performers
   c. a printer's receptacle for discarded type

5. DUTCHMAN
   a. something used to hide structural defects
   b. a type of door
   c. a nautical term for a missing ship

6. EARLOCK
   a. a sailor's knot resembling an ear
   b. a curl of hair by the ear
   c. a regional variation of the word *oarlock*

7. SUPERSEX
   a. a sterile organism having both male and female characteristics

b. feminist coining for the female sex

c. of a sexually satisfying nature

8. SMEARCASE
   a. mechanic's case for storing oily tools before cleaning
   b. a type of cottage cheese
   c. a container for theatrical makeup

9. DAYMARE
   a. horse used as a pacer for morning workouts at race tracks
   b. a nightmarish fantasy experienced while awake
   c. a type of weather characteristic of the horse latitudes

10. DRAGÉE
    a. a member of the Indian elite classes
    b. a sugar-coated nut
    c. something which is transported by dragging

11. TAPSTER
    a. a tap dancer
    b. a tavern keeper or bartender
    c. one engaged in illegal phone surveillance

12. CATCHFLY
    a. an insect-trapping plant
    b. a net behind home plate in baseball stadiums
    c. a bowl of sugared water used in colonial kitchens to trap flies

13. WARMOUTH
    a. an aggressive person
    b. a hawkish or right-wing newspaper
    c. a freshwater fish

Equivokes II

Determine the proper definition for these words.

1. FILMSET
   a. related to photocomposition
   b. members of the motion picture industry
   c. diaphanous scrim used by photographers

2. TOPCROSS
   a. a cross mounted on a steeple
   b. a skiing maneuver
   c. a cross between a purebred male and inferior female stock

3. RIPRAP
   a. to strengthen with a foundation of broken stones
   b. a type of saw
   c. a particularly strong riptide feared by surfers

4. CANFIELD
   a. a garbage dump
   b. a metallic coated arena used by skateboarders
   c. a type of card game

5. PEDIPALP
   a. an orthopedic device
   b. sensory appendage of an arachnid
   c. a type of foot-powered vehicle

6. COYDOG
   a. a hybrid between a coyote and a wild dog
   b. a dog trained to be used in undercover police work, particularly narcotics investigations
   c. a sly person

7. FOOTLER
   a. an inexperienced male servant
   b. one who wastes time
   c. a measuring device used in shoe manufacturing

8. PALETOT
   a. a loose overcoat
   b. an anemic child
   c. a poor financial showing

9. CHAINMAN
   a. a convict
   b. a surveyor's assistant
   c. a specialty trade in jewelry making

10. FLOPOVER
    a. a defect in television reception
    b. a type of omelet
    c. a fast profit made on a commodity exchange by buying and selling almost simultaneously

11. GAPOSIS
    a. coined by *Time* magazine, an information gap
    b. a dental problem characterized by a gap between front incisors
    c. a gap in a row of buttons or snaps

12. BEESWING
    a. a crust on the surface of some old wines
    b. a two-seater swing shaped like the letter "B"
    c. a lightweight wing used on small aircraft

13. QUEENSIDE
    a. the seat placed to the right of a dignitary at formal gatherings, indicating a place of honor
    b. the side of the chessboard containing the file on which the queen sits at the start of a chess game
    c. the port side of a ship, from British naval tradition

• Trivia Word Search •

Ziggurat

Find the name, phrase, or word beginning with the letter "Z" which fits the definitions below. The answers are also hidden in the maze which follows, *except all the Z's have been removed*. The words can be traced, using any adjacent letters, whether above, below, beside, or diagonal to. *No letter can be used more than once*, and there are no extra letters. Your answer may zigzag through the maze. Obviously, you can also use the maze to find answers you may be uncertain about.

1. From German, meaning the spirit of the time *ZEITGEIST*
2. Strangely spelled teething rusk
3. Character in many horror movies *ZOMBIE*
4. Nothing, zero *ZILCH*
5. Drought-resistant grass
6. Led *ZEPPELIN* , "Stairway to Heaven"
7. Swiss city *ZURICH*
8. His follies made him famous. (last name) *ZIEGFIELD*
9. Spaceman's weightlessness *ZERO GRAVITY*
10. *Viva* this Mexican revolutionary! *ZAPATA*
11. "Top of the line" American appliance? *ZENITH*
12. A photographer would probably have this. *ZOOM LENS*

13. A gentle breeze ZEPHYR

14. Prolific garden vegetable ZUCCHINI

15. Originally Zone Improvement Plan ZIP CODE

16. Describing an abundantly endowed female ZAFTIG

17. Dry red table wine ZINFANDEL

18. Retro (1940s) men's wear ZOOT SUIT

19. "Religion" of the Beat Generation ZEN BUDDHISM

20. Movement which led to establishment of Israel ZIONISM

E	R	R	I	N	E	L	T	M	S
O	G	A	V	F	D	I	O	N	I
A	Y	T	I	A	N	U	I	M	S
P	A	T	A	E	O	S	D	H	I
E	N	S	O	D	O	T	D	U	B
T	I	N	C	F	T	I	G	E	N
H	E	I	P	A	H	I	I	L	D
O	L	U	C	C	R	N	I	E	H
O	M	E	P	H	Y	F	N	I	C
E	I	B	M	I	E	G	I	U	R
G	E	I	O	I	L	C	L	E	P
I	T	S	B	A	K	H	S	I	P
E	T	W	I	E	C	O	Y	A	E

"Y" Knot

The answers to these trivia questions all begin with the letter "Y." When you've figured out the answers, look for them in the maze below. *All the Y's have been removed from the words.* The words in the maze can be traced, using any adjacent letters, whether above, below, beside, or diagonal. *No letter can be used more than once*, and there are no extra letters. Your answer may zigzag through the maze. Obviously, you can also use the maze to find answers you may be uncertain about.

1. Home of Old Faithful

2. Great dance song by The Village People

3. Disease which hindered building the Panama Canal

4. Flowering plant whose dried stalks are sometimes used to cast the *I Ching*

5. Scene of historical conference in February 1945, attended by Stalin, Churchill, and Roosevelt

6. Irish poet, playwright, winner of Nobel Prize, 1923 (full name)

7. Classic English accompaniment to roast beef

8. Day of atonement

9. Song popular during the American Revolution

10. Passive female principle and active masculine principle in Chinese philosophy

11. A Hindu discipline which involves a stylized system of exercise to promote control of mind and body

12. Cultured milk product

13. A Japanese dish consisting of skewered and grilled pieces of chicken

14. Country at the southwestern tip of the Arabian peninsula

15. Neil Simon play, *Lost in* _____

16. A one-year-old thoroughbred race horse

17. Christmas time

E	S	E	E	L	D	E	E	P	I
M	R	U	K	D	O	K	U	P	K
E	L	G	N	O	I	N	R	M	O
N	E	N	O	G	N	A	A	I	L
E	T	I	A	O	A	B	M	I	L
D	I	L	N	A	N	U	W	O	W
E	A	R	G	D	L	T	A	R	R
R	I	T	O	G	E	T	A	W	A
O	T	R	G	N	R	L	F	O	L
I	K	U	I	A	E	E	E	E	L
A	U	D	D	T	R	V	E	S	W
P	R	S	K	S	A	N	T	L	O
E	I	H	R	O	C	M	O	L	E

OD'd on "O"

The answers to these trivia questions are words or phrases which all begin with the letter "O." When you've determined the answers, you can look for them in the letter maze which follows. *All the initial O's have been removed from the words in the maze.* The words in the maze can be traced, using any adjacent letters, whether above, below, beside, or diagonal to. *No letter can be used more than once*, and there are no extra letters. Your answer may zigzag through the maze. Obviously, you can also use the maze to help you find answers you may be uncertain about.

1. Historic overland route to the West, beginning at the Missouri River

2. Beloved of Eurydice

3. Filmdom's top award

4. Titania's husband (*Midsummer Night's Dream*)

5. Remote Australian countryside

6. Exotic flower

7. Athletic happening in 1996, 2000, 2004

8. Pertaining to the sense of smell

9. Unfortunately related to Jocasta

10. Venerable English university

11. Planned _____, outmoded on purpose

12. Roman poet, author of *Ars Amatoria*

13. Did he act alone on November 22, 1963? (full name)

14. Was Dogpatch located in these hilly uplands of Missouri?

15. To kiss

16. Collectively, islands of Central and South Pacific

17. The Sooner state

18. In Egyptian mythology, god of the underworld, husband-brother of Isis

Y	S	W	S	U	L	A	S	R	S
E	V	A	C	L	K	H	I	I	A
L	R	L	D	A	A	I	O	M	D
E	A	A	R	T	E	N	A	R	O
E	H	Z	K	S	C	E	S	X	F
C	E	N	V	I	Y	P	U	S	I
S	E	C	E	D	R	I	D	C	P
L	O	S	B	T	O	E	L	Y	M
L	F	A	C	B	E	N	H	P	R
D	I	A	B	R	O	E	R	T	O
H	C	C	T	A	S	U	A	N	G
R	K	U	R	C	S	L	I	R	E

Valedictorian

The answers to these trivia questions all begin with the letter "V." When you've figured out the answers, look for them again in the letter maze which follows. *All the initial V's have been removed from the words in the maze.* The words can be traced, using any adjacent letters, whether above, below, beside, or diagonal. *No letter can be used more than once*, and there are no extra letters. Your answer may zigzag through the maze. You can also use the maze to find answers you may be uncertain about.

1. Profession of James Herriot

2. Animal having a backbone

3. Mistress of Merlin (the Lady of the Lake)

4. Composer of *The Four Seasons*

5. Anne Rice antihero

6. Nature abhors this

7. Subject of many Chevy Chase movies

8. Satirical Thackeray novel

9. Setting of *Romeo and Juliet*

10. May 8th, 1945

11. International United States government radio

12. A master of technique in the arts

13. Police division charged with combatting prostitution, gambling

14. Another name for a snake

15. A tramp
16. Papal seat in Rome
17. "Dizzy" Hitchcock film
18. Late-afternoon or evening prayers
19. Enjoyed as a result of imaginary participation
20. Eating predilection of G. B. Shaw

V	I	F	A	M	I	V	A	L	I
I	N	O	E	R	I	R	T	D	I
A	I	E	C	I	S	O	U	E	P
O	C	A	E	R	O	E	R	R	I
E	R	T	E	T	E	T	I	R	A
O	G	I	S	P	B	E	N	A	N
A	F	Y	O	E	R	A	T	E	E
I	Y	T	N	I	R	S	N	O	R
R	A	I	A	T	M	U	A	E	G
E	D	N	A	C	A	U	A	T	E
C	A	R	I	A	C	E	R	I	A
I	Q	U	O	N	T	R	N	A	N
S	E	A	U	A	R	I	M	C	T
I	C	D	S	A	G	P	A	I	A

T Square

The answers to the following trivia questions all begin with the letter "T." When you've found the answers, find them again in the letter maze which follows. *All the initial T's have been removed from the words in the maze.* The words can be traced, using adjoining letters whether above, below, beside or diagonal. *No letter can be used more than once,* and there are no extra letters. You can also use the maze to find answers you may be uncertain about.

1. Christian holiday celebrated on January 5th

2. An English square

3. It's a devil

4. Yolky painting medium

5. Shores in Marine Corps anthem

6. Transportation to a beheading

7. In a teapot?

8. John Gotti, the _____ Don

9. Toy named after a U.S. President

10. *Rex* of *Jurassic Park*

11. "She sells seashells" is one

12. Caused by the Helen-Paris fling

13. Thor Heyerdahl's Kon

14. Every three years

15. Male hormone

16. Provable proposition in math

17. Landed Dorothy in Oz

18. Archipelago at extreme tip of South America, "land of fire"

19. Opposed to Whig

20. Gulf, northwestern arm of the China Sea, pivotal in United States history

E	S	T	A	D	D	E	L	N	N
T	S	O	N	O	A	E	F	I	E
E	R	O	R	R	O	G	U	A	I
E	N	O	O	R	O	N	L	R	R
H	E	R	E	E	K	I	R	Y	A
R	A	W	M	I	N	O	I	B	E
J	A	N	E	T	I	K	Y	D	D
R	O	R	W	I	S	P	O	L	E
G	U	E	R	U	S	I	R	A	I
O	N	S	A	U	U	R	E	P	M
N	N	O	O	N	M	G	A	R	E
A	R	L	L	R	B	L	A	F	A
Y	E	F	E	A	M	G	H	T	R
S	E	P	N	N	S	I	T	F	L
T	E	M	A	I	A	N	H	W	E

• Relatively Speaking •

My Cousin Charley

My cousin Charley loves words and word play. Everything he does centers around words, word patterns, puns, and general tomfoolery having to do with dictionaries and word guides. Discover some of his quirks and unmask the word tricks in these sentences. In the first sentence, for example, the words *dialogue* and *euphoria* contain all the vowels—*a, e, i, o, u.*

1. He can dialogue with euphoria, but he cannot discourse with enthusiasm.

2. He named his cats Munster and Sternum, rejecting our suggestions of Monster and Stewbum.

3. He reads *Moby Dick* but not *Billy Budd*. He loves *Jane Eyre* but hates *Wuthering Heights*.

4. He will wear chinos but not khakis. He will listen to a cello but not to a bass viola. He will believe a ghost is in the house but definitely will not accept the thought of an apparition.

5. He loves the cancan but hates French dancing. He loves a good bonbon but hates candy.

6. He bids "adieu" but won't say "goodbye." He keeps his clothes in a bureau but won't use a dresser.

7. He will pout when he has the gout and complain when he has a pain, but he won't fuss over his health.

Charley's Cats

When my cousin Charley got his new cats, Munster and Sternum, he nearly drove us mad. For months he sprinkled his conversation with nine-letter words (for nine lives, get it?) containing the word *cat*. Of course, there were big gaps in his speech while he searched his encyclopedic vocabulary for the right word for each occasion. Try to extriCATe from the clues below the nine-letter words Charley used to give us all CATalepsy.

1. The only kind of church he would go into was a _____.

2. His sailboat was a specific kind, a _____.

3. He wouldn't drink rieslings, or any other wines but _____.

4. He did not utter an obscenity, but instead became obsessed with _____.

5. Quite the athlete, Charley participated in a _____.

6. He didn't chew his food, he would only _____ it.

7. When he needed new glasses, he told us he hoped he wasn't developing _____.

8. When he took his pills, Charley told us he was now properly _____.

9. Worried about a breathing problem the cats had, Charley told us that they would not _____.

10. He wouldn't oil his car, he would _____ it.

Charley's Aunts

My cousin Charley had a strange relationship with the rest of the family. To find out how you stood with him, you had to be great at anagrams. For years, he blithely called one of his mother's sisters *Aunt Eased* until she figured out Charley's nickname for her was an anagram for *nauseated*. Find the anagram of these aunts' names to discover the hidden quality, trait, or occupation which piqued Charley's interest.

1. AUNT HERHED worked for an employment agency.

2. AUNT GROAN had a very simian appearance.

3. AUNT CLORN never went out during the day.

4. AUNT PROMA worked for a major motion picture studio.

5. AUNT SERES loved fine wines.

6. AUNT CORER told a great story.

7. AUNT BLERT used to be a deejay.

8. AUNT FADIR once worked for Ralph Nader.

9. AUNT LEFTL was not a person you wanted to be in an enclosed space with.

10. AUNT ALTAR was hairy and scary.

11. AUNT DEBET once had a coming-out party.

12. AUNT BODIC was once kidnapped.

13. AUNT ASTOR was very spacey.

14. AUNT DENNS always wintered in Florida.

Charley's Uncles

Charley's uncles, like most of the aunts, never figured out what Charley thought about them. *Uncle Meow* never knew the letters in his nickname were an anagram for *unwelcome*. Here's your chance to uncover family secrets. Find the anagrams of the uncles' names to discover the quality, trait, or occupation which Charley hid.

1. UNCLE ICY used an unusual mode of transportation.

2. UNCLE AIRT chewed a lot of Tums.

3. UNCLE PORT could stand to lose a few pounds.

4. UNCLE BANDA couldn't walk a straight line, even when sober.

5. UNCLE KISS won the lottery.

6. UNCLE AMIS thought he was very manly.

7. UNCLE THIM loved to eat at noon.

8. UNCLE AMBA was very accident-prone.

9. UNCLE AITH, the lawyer, was something of a shyster.

10. UNCLE DORS was an unprincipled rascal.

11. UNCLE SCUT was "full of juice."

12. UNCLE RESS was downright mean.

13. UNCLE FAFE had more money than anyone else in the family.

14. UNCLE ORSO was always dispensing unwanted advice.

Cousinly

The cousins, of course, fit into Charley's anagram scheme. *Cousin DT*, an anagram for the word *discount*, liked to shop for bargains. See if you can determine why Charley gave the nicknames below to the rest of his large tribe of cousins. Figure out the anagrams of the cousins' names to make sense of Charley's cousin-naming game.

1. COUSIN SIP works as a detective.

2. COUSIN URI was always very uninterested.

3. COUSIN LES wants to be alone.

4. COUSIN RET comes from a long line of eccentrics who could use a little psychoanalysis.

5. COUSIN REX loves trips.

6. COUSIN TAD spends a lot of time with broomsticks.

7. COUSIN G. T. loves camporees.

8. COUSIN TED is quite the ladies' man.

9. COUSIN OLL likes to plot with other people in illegal schemes. He's been in jail.

10. COUSIN V. T. is an English nobleman.

11. COUSIN FON is really bewildering.

12. COUSIN TEA is very dogged.

13. COUSIN GAR loves to party.

14. COUSIN LIN is always saying, "Count me in!"

15. COUSIN TENTO loves to fight.

Aunt Amelia Visits the Zoo

Aunt Amelia kept a journal of all the animals she saw by writing down an anagram of each. Can you decipher her list?

Example: CAROB   C O B R A

  1. BRAZE   _____

  2. FLOW   _____

  3. POPISH   _____

  4. TORTE   _____

  5. PAROLED   _____

  6. COOLEST   _____

  7. CORONA   _____

  8. MANIAC   _____

  9. ROOTIEST _____

10. OOCYTE   _____

Zoologist Level

11. PATINA   _____

12. AMASSING   _____

Aunt Amelia Visits the Dog Show

Aunt Amelia kept a journal of all the dogs she saw by creating an anagram of each one. Can you decipher her list?

Example: RETAG DEAN   G R E A T   D A N E

  1. SPOOLED   _____

  2. ORGIC   _____

  3. PROTEIN   _____

  4. RISHI RETIRER   _____   _____

  5. PAINLESS   _____

  6. SATIN BRANDER

      _____   _____

  7. SOMEDAY   _____

  8. BEASTS UNSHOD

      _____   _____

  9. SHINGLE TESTERS

      _____   _____

 10. LARBOARD   _____

Aunt Amelia Visits the Aviary

Aunt Amelia kept a journal of all the birds she saw by creating an anagram of each one. Can you decipher her list?

Example: ROGUES   G R O U S E

1. RENT _____
2. GREET _____
3. HONER _____
4. MISPAGE _____
5. CORDON _____
6. EPIGON _____
7. BRAWLER _____
8. PANICLE _____
9. HOEDOWN _____
10. HORMONE _____

Ornithologist Level

11. TIME-OUTS _____
12. BROKAGES _____

Aunt Amelia Visits the Aquarium

Aunt Amelia kept a journal of all the creatures she saw by creating an anagram of each one. Can you decipher her list?

Example: TUTOR   <u>T R O U T</u>

 1. CALM   _____

 2. STOREY   _____

 3. AUNT   _____

 4. HARKS   _____

 5. GULLIBLE   _____

 6. SANDIER   _____

 7. BOLSTER   _____

 8. FISHBOWL   _____

 9. UNFOLDER   _____

10. STRAYING   _____

11. BALANCER   _____

12. EMANATE   _____

13. SUMLESS   _____

Aunt Amelia Visits the Botanic Garden

Aunt Amelia kept a journal of all flowers she saw by creating an anagram of each one. Can you decipher her list?

Example: PROMISER   P R I M R O S E

1. TEARS   _____
2. SAYID   _____
3. MUSED   _____
4. AVAILS   _____
5. LINEUP   _____
6. OCCURS   _____
7. SUPINATE   _____
8. RELOANED   _____
9. MEASURING   _____
10. CLIMATES   _____
11. TERMLY   _____

Green Thumb Level

12. STABILE   _____
13. FAERIES   _____

• Trivia •

Lit*mus* Test

Uncle Sylvester, after listening to too many U.S. Senate hearings, became infatuated with the litmus test. He asks you to identify these literary references which contain "mus." He's no ignora*mus*!

1. Associated with rabbit tales

   — — — — —   — — — — —

2. French author of *The Stranger*

   — — — — — —   — — — — —

3. *La Bohème* character — — — — — — —

4. Dumas swashbuckler — — — — — — — — —

5. "Dublin Fair City" comestible — — — — — — —

6. Chaplin trademark — — — — — — — —

7. Greek god of censure and mockery — — — — —

8. Private-eye moniker — — — — — —

9. American art form, evolved from vaudeville

   — — — — — —

10. Alice ate this — — — — — — — —

11. Nine inspiring Greek ladies — — — — —

12. Frenchman (1503–1556) known for his predictions

    — — — — — — — — — —

Lit Test

Many characters in literature, myth, and biblical history are drawn in such a lively way that they have entered our language as nouns and adjectives descriptive of types and classes of people. Test your literary I.Q. with this quiz.

1. From Jonathan Swift's land of little people, used to describe a diminutive or petty person. _____ (adjective)

2. From an American folktale, used to describe someone or something very large. _____ (adjective)

3. Any young woman who comes into good fortune after a period of adversity, from a classic fairy tale. _____ (noun)

4. From the New Testament, one who betrays another under the guise of friendship. _____ (noun)

5. From the Roman god of wine, now used to describe a drunken or carousing person or event. _____ (adjective)

6. A person of extraordinary strength or agility, from Edgar Rice Burroughs hero. _____ (noun)

7. From Dickens, a person who instructs another in crime. _____ (noun)

8. A lament, tale of woe, or complaint, from Old Testament prophet. _____ (noun)

9. A bold and scheming woman, from biblical wife of Ahab. _____ (noun)

• Trivia Anagrams •

What's in a Name?

Creating an anagram from the letters in a celebrity's name sometimes forms interesting phrases vaguely related to the person's attributes, circumstances, role, or occupation. Unscramble each phrase below to discover these famous people—past and present.

Example: LO, HIP SEÑORA   S o p h i a   L o r e n

1. DO BE IN TERROR

— — — — — —   — — — — — —

2. FILLY LEADS __ __ __ __   __ — — — —

3. HATED FOR ILL

— — — — —   — — — — — —

4. DESERVE TO WIN

— — — — — —   — — — — — —

5. I MAIL ESTROGEN

— — — — — —   — — — — — —

6. PAY FOR WHINER

— — — — —   — — — — — — —

7. ENTREATS VIM __ __ __ __ __   — — — — — — —

8. SO, I ACT; LED TOWN

— — — — —   — — — — — — — —

9. OH, HAD LINEUP __ __ __ __   — — — — — — — —

70

What's in a Name II?
Know the Write People

Creating an anagram from the letters in a celebrity's name sometimes forms interesting phrases vaguely related to the person's attributes, circumstances or a character or work they have created. Unscramble each phrase below to discover the well-known, not necessarily contemporary, author.

1. A MANLIER NORM

 — — — — — —   — — — — — —

2. A LONE PALE DREG

 — — — — —   — — — — — —   — — —

3. SEE AWRY MEN THING

 — — — — — —   — — — — — — — — —

4. RAD CLUES IN THORO YARN __ __ __

 — — — — — —   — — — — —   — — — — — —

5. I'M SICKLY, DONE IN

 — — — — —   — — — — — — — — — —

6. HAD ONE HARDY VIRTUE __ __ __ __ __

 — — — — —   — — — — — — — —

7. ALIENIST MEWLS SEEN

 — — — — — — — — —   — — — — — — — —

8. AH, AIRTIGHT CASE

 — — — — — —   — — — — — — — —

9. HANDWROTE HIT

 — — — — —   — — — — — — —

Global Power

Anagram each word below to find the name of a country—past or present.

Example: PENAL   <u>N e p a l</u>

1. PURE   _____

2. RAIN   _____

3. REIGN   _____

4. RUMBA   _____

5. BIALY   _____

6. LAITY   _____

7. ERECT   _____

8. PINAS   _____

9. ENEMY   _____

10. SAILER   _____

11. ASPIRE   _____

12. ANALOG   _____

13. REGALIA   _____

14. INLACED   _____

15. PENALTIES   _____

Bonus: Many country names are also uncapitalized words with other meanings, for example, *China.* How many country names that are also acceptable words can you find? Compare your answers with our list of sixteen. Ten is a super score!

Global Power II

Anagram each word below to find the name of large cities in different parts of the world.

Example: PANELS   <u>N a p l e s</u>, Italy

1. SALVAGES   _ _ _   _ _ _ _ _
2. INWARD   _ _ _ _ _ _
3. UNITS   _ _ _ _ _
4. EVINCE   _ _ _ _ _ _
5. GOALS   _ _ _ _ _
6. DOTTIER   _ _ _ _ _ _ _
7. HASTEN   _ _ _ _ _ _
8. VALIANCE   _ _ _ _ _ _ _ _
9. LOUSE   _ _ _ _ _
10. DELES   _ _ _ _ _
11. DIAGNOSE   _ _ _   _ _ _ _ _
12. SAUNAS   _ _ _ _ _ _
13. COUNTS   _ _ _ _ _ _
14. CASCARA   _ _ _ _ _ _ _
15. GASOLENES   _ _ _   _ _ _ _ _ _ _

Global Power III

Anagram each set of letters below to find the name of large cities in different parts of the world. Believe it or not, each of these cities is also an acceptable word with another meaning.

Example: A A C E G H N O R   <u>A n c h o r a g e</u>,
           Alaska, U.S.A.

1. AADMRS   _____

2. ABHT   _____

3. DELOOT   _____

4. ABFFLOU   _____

5. AIPRS   _____

6. AARSWW   _____

7. CDEEINOPRV   _____

8. EHINOPX   _____

9. AAILMN   _____

10. ABGHMRU   _____

11. ABDEORUX   _____

12. ACIIORTV   _____

• Anagrams •

Symbolically Speaking

:   .   *   +   %   ]   ,   /

Use *one* of the symbols above as a base word along with the extra letters designated, to discover the word indicated in the clue.

Example: __ and P = movie featuring a mermaid
/ (SLASH) and P = <u>Splash</u>

1. __ and V = to furnish or supply

2. __ and Y = a territory settled in a distant land

3. __ and E = rhythmic pattern of heartbeat tested at wrist

4. __ and M = those who misunderstand

5. __ and S = a support for the spinal area

6. __ and R = to eat or drink in a noisy manner

7. __ and U = not very hip

8. __ and H K = a nice place to spend a summer afternoon

9. __ and B I = one who speaks spitefully or slanderously about another person

10. __ and A V = Stromboli, for one

11. __ and E J = some drinks popular in the southern U.S.

Want Adz from A to Z

Each of these twenty-six words is an anagram for a single word, and each answer starts with a different letter of the alphabet. Use the chart below to keep track of the initial letter of each anagram.

1. FINKED _____
2. MINGLER _____
3. GROUTY _____
4. RAGWEED _____
5. TRAVEL _____
6. TEETHES _____
7. DEMISED _____
8. BRAILLE _____
9. TABLET _____
10. SIX _____
11. UNPOSTED _____
12. DOZEN _____
13. APLENTY _____
14. MANTRAP _____
15. IRKSOME _____
16. LIMPED _____
17. SMARTER _____
18. MUNDANE _____
19. LOUDEN _____
20. INFESTS _____
21. PATCHES _____
22. GYRATED _____
23. SOUPÇON _____
24. TRIJET _____
25. TENSION _____
26. REQUIRE _____

A	B	C	D	E	F	G	H	I	J	K	L	M	N	O	P	Q	R	S	T	U	V	W	X	Y	Z

Want Adz II, Short List

Each of these words is an anagram and has only one solution. Each starts with a different letter of the alphabet. Use the chart below to keep track of the initial letter of each anagram.

1. INFLATOR _____

2. SIMPLEST _____

3. ROASTING _____

4. NOBLESSE _____

5. RIVALING _____

6. SPECTRUM _____

7. CAVIARE _____

8. MINUTELY _____

9. REVOLUTE _____

10. METERING _____

11. REQUITAL _____

12. MONODIES _____

13. POUCHIER _____

14. DRAINAGE _____

15. DESPITES _____

16. RAPIDER _____

17. CHESTIER _____

18. MISWROTE _____

19. TIDINESS _____

20. RETITLED _____

21. TREATY _____

22. INCENSES _____

A	B	C	D	E	F	G	H	I	J	K	L	M	N	O	P	Q	R	S	T	U	V	W	X	Y	Z

Want Adz III, Short List

Each of these words is an anagram and has only one solution. Each starts with a different letter of the alphabet. Use the chart below to keep track of the initial letter of each anagram.

1. DEMURRER _____

2. ROSEOLA _____

3. MONEYBAG _____

4. OUTCURSE _____

5. NATIVISM _____

6. SQUATTER _____

7. TOPSOIL _____

8. PROPOSE _____

9. PIMENTOS _____

10. DOWERIES _____

11. DRAYMEN _____

12. SHARING _____

13. STEEPLED _____

14. MUTILATE _____

15. REFINING _____

16. INTERRED _____

17. DISPLODE _____

18. MOONIEST _____

19. EPITAPHS _____

20. UNDERFED _____

21. FINISHED _____

22. HUSTLING _____

A	B	C	D	E	F	G	H	I	J	K	L	M	N	O	P	Q	R	S	T	U	V	W	X	Y	Z

Dog Catcher

Keeping the order given, add the letters D O G (not necessarily in that order) to the strings of letters below to catch some common words.

Example: R A N S N   GranDsOn

1. I R L H O

2. E V U R I N

3. K N W L E E

4. R U N H O G

5. W N R A D E

6. W R N O E R

7. R A N F L Y

8. E X P L I N

9. V A A B N

10. S H A W I N

11. L E N R O D

12. C N E S T E

13. R A I O L Y

14. B A N W A N

15. M R T A G E

16. B L I A T E

17. U I E B O K

18. U N E R N E

19. R A N E A E

20. H Y R E N

21. H E A L N

22. M A R I L

23. I A N S I S

24. P R I I E S

Manhunt

Keeping the order given, add the letters M A N (not necessarily in that order) to the strings of letters below to discover the common words hidden in this MANHUNT.

Example: A R T H O   MarAthoN

1. B D O I A L

2. I G I A R Y

3. C A R O I

4. L E B R A I

5. L I G A N T

6. D Y I T E

7. I P T I E T

8. F L I G O

9. I P O R T T

10. G R O P H O E

11. S P E R I T

12. E O T I O L

13. B E C H R K

14. A B O R L

15. S C R A E T

16. C I E T I C

17. D O I N C E

18. G E R I U

19. C H I E R Y

20. R I S T O R

21. E O P U S E

22. G E T I C

23. C O E D I

24. E U E R T E

• Category Puzzles •

Joint Custody

Find the one word that combines, in front or back, with each word in each set below to form a phrase, name, title, or compound word.

Example: SHOT, BLUE, THIRSTY, MOBILE <u>blood</u>
           BLOODshot, blueBLOOD, BLOODthirsty,
           BLOODmobile

1. REAR, PICTURE, DRESSING, WASHER

2. DOG, WHITE, DRESS, HOLD

3. CASTLE, STORM, BAG, MAN

4. TALKS, BAG, MARKET, FUNNY

5. MEAL, KNOT, DANCE, ROOT

6. ROSE, WHACK, LEAGUE, GEORGE

7. ORGAN, PEACE, DOWN, DREAM

8. DUST, BROWN, GHOST, CRABBE

9. PARADISE, CAP, GOLD, ERRAND

10. FAITH, DATE, SPOT, DUCK

Joint Custody II

Find the one word that combines, in front or back, with each word in each set below to form a phrase, name, title, or compound word.

Example: HALL, TAP, SQUARE, OF DEATH   <u>dance</u>
DANCE hall, tap DANCE, square DANCE, DANCE of death

1. MARKET, DOG, DOZER, PAPAL

2. COPY, NIP, TAIL, WALK

3. TAG, CHILl, HANG, UNDER

4. HOUSE, EYED, LITTER, DOODLE

5. VIRGIN, CONTROL, MARK, STONE

6. SHORT, CREW, GLASS, UPPER

7. POSTER, SCORE, H, FLUSHER

8. HOLE, GLOVE, HOUND, FIRE

9. CREAM, HOCKEY, CAP, BREAKER

10. EXPOSURE, HEMISPHERE, IRELAND, LIGHTS

Joint Custody III

Find the one word that combines, in front or back, with each word in each set below to form a phrase, name, title, or compound word.

Example: GUN, BLUE, PUFF, FACE   <u>powder</u>
gunPOWDER, POWDER blue, POWDER puff, face POWDER

1. SEA, GAME, SHOCK, FISH

2. CHICKEN, FEVER, BOARD, WATER

3. HEADED, LATIN, PORKY, STY

4. POTION, AFFAIR, SEAT, TRUE

5. CHEST, DIAMOND, LESS, BOB

6. SLIPPER, HOUSES, LOOKING, MENAGERIE

7. SLIDE, EEL, ORGAN, CHAIR

8. HOT, FAMINE, SWEET, CHIP

9. STATES, NATIONS, PRESS INTERNATIONAL, KINGDOM

10. CAR, JACKET, GUN, NO

Joint Custody IV

Find the one word that combines, in front or back, with each word in each set below to form a phrase, name, title, or compound word.

Example: HORSE, FOAM, LEGS, MONSTER   <u>sea</u>
           SEA horse, SEA foam, SEA legs, SEA monster

1. GREEN, NAIL, TACK, SCREW

2. BITE, ROBERT, JACK, HOAR

3. OMELET, SPAGHETTI, FRONT, FRONTIER

4. SAUCER, BUTTRESS, FEAR OF, COLORS

5. BEER, SNAP, ROGERS, BREAD

6. MUFFIN, BODY, LANGUAGE, CHANNEL

7. SILVER, BREAD, FED, TABLE

8. ATTACK, BEAN, CLOCKWISE, ESPIONAGE

9. DRESSING, DOORS, TOAST, FRIES

10. FATHER, BOMB, CAPSULE, IMMEMORIAL

Joint Custody V

Find the one word that combines, in front or back, with each word in each set below to form a phrase, name, title, or compound word.

Example: JOY, UP, BROOM, PIN   <u>stick</u>
           joySTICK, STICKup, broomSTICK, STICKpin

1. RADISH, POWER, SHOE, SENSE

2. ABOUT, LIFT, TYPE, BOLD

3. GUESS, STRING, CHILDHOOD, NATURE

4. ROAD, BOAT, BUSINESS, PLACE

5. TUBE, CITY, SANCTUM, DIRECTED

6. DELIGHT, TOWEL, BATH, EMPIRE

7. BRICK, BOY, VAMPIRE, DING

8. SUPREME, JESTER, HOUSE, MARTIAL

9. BORN, SPIRIT, LANCE, GERM

10. BROTHER, THE SUNDANCE, GLOVES, SKIN

Common Denominator

Divide the list of items below into five categories of three items each. Use each item just once. Some items may fit into more than one category, but only one solution uses all words.

BANANAS	KERMIT	SOCIETY
CANARY	MANHATTAN	TOILET BOWL
CHEESE	MONEY	TOOTH
COFFEE	PAINT	VIRGIN
GRASS	SLEEPER	WEDDING

Category <u>Things That Are Green</u> : <u>grass,</u> _____

and _____.

Category _____ : _____, _____

and _____.

Category _____ : _____, _____

and _____.

Category _____ : _____, _____

and _____.

Category _____ : _____, _____

and _____.

Common Denominator II

Divide the list of names below into five categories of three items each. Use each name just once. Some may fit into more than one category, but only one solution uses all names.

ALLEN	DUDLEY	MARY
CHER	ETHEL	MARY TYLER
DEAN	GUTHRIE	PRINCE
DEMI	LIONEL	STEVE
DREW	MADONNA	WOODPECKER

Category Moores : Demi, _____

and _____.

Category _____ : _____, _____

and _____.

Category _____ : _____, _____

and _____.

Category _____ : _____, _____

and _____.

Category _____ : _____, _____

and _____.

Common Denominator III

Divide the list of items below into five categories of three items each. Use each item just once. Some items may fit into more than one category, but only one solution uses all words.

FLINT	DEAD BODY	PEANUTS
JERK	FROST	GALL
GINGER	ROLLING	SARSAPARILLA
BURNS	JACK	PONY
FLARE	BROWNING	MASHED POTATO

Category Stones : Rolling, _____

and _____.

Category _____ : _____, _____

and _____.

Category _____ : _____, _____

and _____.

Category _____ : _____, _____

and _____.

Category _____ : _____, _____

and _____.

Common Denominator IV

Divide the list of items below into five categories of three items each. Use each item just once. Some items may fit into more than one category, but only one solution uses all words.

GUITAR   IPANEMA   JULIA
MIAMI   SUNFLOWER   TRAIN
COTTON   COLD   OMAHA
FEVER   RITA   COWARD
FISH   NOSE   MICHELLE

Category "Yellow" Things : sunflower, _____

and _____.

Category _____ : _____, _____

and _____.

Category _____ : _____, _____

and _____.

Category _____ : _____, _____

and _____.

Category _____ : _____, _____

and _____.

Common Denominator V

Divide the list of items below into five categories of three items each. Use each item just once. Some items may fit into more than one category, but only one solution uses all words.

BALANCHINE	ANNE	POMPIDOU
SIMON	RAY CHARLES	JOHN
EMILY	ROUND	HELEN KELLER
OEDIPUS REX	THOMAS	FLANK
CHUCK	HARRISON	CHARLOTTE

Category <u>Brontë Sisters</u> : <u>Emily,</u> _____

and _____.

Category _____ : _____, _____

and _____.

Category _____ : _____, _____

and _____.

Category _____ : _____, _____

and _____.

Category _____ : _____, _____

and _____.

Common Denominator VI

Divide the list of items below into five categories of three items each. Use each item just once. Some items may fit into more than one category, but only one solution uses all words.

BLOOD PRESSURE	KISS	BUBBLE
AIR	JUNK	ZIPPER
CANYON	MARRIAGE	SLAM
POETIC	PIANO	REGISTERED
NOSE	DOG	ELEVATOR

Category Things That Go Up : elevator, _____ and _____.

Category _____ : _____, _____ and _____.

Category _____ : _____, _____ and _____.

Category _____ : _____, _____ and _____.

Category _____ : _____, _____ and _____.

• Letter Patterns •

Angelic Devilry

Insert all the letters, not necessarily in order, from the word ANGEL or DEVIL in the blanks below to form acceptable words.

Example: C O N G E N I A L
              C I V I L I Z E D

1. J __ __ __ __ __

2. __ E __ __ R __ __

3. __ O __ __ B __ R __

4. __ __ __ __ C __

5. __ __ S S O __ __ __

6. __ __ __ U __ G __ D

7. __ A S __ __ __ __

8. __ A N __ A __ __ Z __

9. A __ O __ __ A B __ __

10. H __ __ O __ __ __

11. __ E __ __ __ __

12. __ __ S O __ I __ __

13. __ R __ __ __ __

14. __ I __ __ __ __ E

15. __ __ __ __ __ O E R

16. F I __ __ __ __ __ D

17. __ __ __ I __ __

18. __ __ __ R __ I __ S T

92

Guys & Gals

Insert all the letters, not necessarily in order, from the word GUY or GAL in the blanks below to form acceptable words.

Example: H U R R Y I N G
H O L O G R A M

1. __ __ I L T __

2. F L __ __ P O __ E

3. B O D __ __ __ A R D

4. T __ N __ E __ O

5. S I N __ U __ __ R

6. B U R __ __ N D __

7. S __ N A __ O G __ E

8. __ O __ N __

9. H __ N __ N A I __

10. __ __ U __ H T E R

11. __ A __ Z __

12. S __ __ A R __

13. __ O __ __ R T

14. L A D __ B __ __

15. E __ E __ __ N T

16. N E __ R O L O __ __

17. H O O __ I __ __ N

18. __ __ R N E __

Twofers

Use all the letters from one of the two words (such as *award* or *night* in the first set) below, not necessarily in the order given, to fill in the blanks and decipher hidden words. These puzzles use common words, but being aware of common prefixes, suffixes, and word patterns will help you.

Answers to Challenge questions may be proper names. They do not necessarily draw on letters from these key words.

Award Night

Example: A N Y t h i n g   H a R d w a r E

1. __ W K __ __ __ __ L Y
2. __ U __ __ R __ E S __
3. L E __ __ __ __ __ E R
4. W __ I S __ L __ __ __
5. B O __ __ __ __ __ L K

6. H __ __ D S I __ __ __
7. __ __ S H B O __ __ __
8. __ R __ O __ H E __ __
9. __ F T E R __ __ __ __
10. G U __ F __ __ __ __

Challenge: What is the highest U.S. award (perhaps comparable to the Academy Award) given for achievement in advertising?

Coca-Cola (Coca and Cola)

Example: a c c o R D I O N   D I P l o M a c Y

1. __ L __ __ H O L I __
2. B __ __ H E __ __ R
3. I L __ __ G I __ __ L

4. S T __ __ K __ __ R
5. C __ __ K R O __ __ H
6. W __ S H __ __ __ T H

7. D E M __ __ R __ __ Y   9. __ R __ S S W __ __ K

8. S __ __ R E __ __ R D   10. __ __ A T R __ __ K

Challenge: What parts of the cola tree yield the extract used in the manufacture of cola drinks?

Moby Dick

Example: m o N E y b A G   G R i d L O c k

1. T __ __ __ O __   6. H __ __ N __ __ O K

2. B A __ __ S __ __ E   7. S __ __ E K I __ __

3. __ U __ __ L __ N G   8. B __ __ __ E R E __

4. H __ __ E __ O D __   9. S __ __ __ __ L I C

5. H A N __ P __ __ __   10. W __ __ __ E __ L Y

Challenge: What is the famous sentence which begins Herman Melville's classic novel *Moby Dick*?

Santa Claus

Example: F a n a t I C s   c a l C U L u s

1. __ __ __ __ Z __   6. __ O __ __ __ L G I __

2. __ G __ I __ __ __   7. __ P __ __ __ __ E

3. M __ __ I __ __ __   8. M __ __ __ __ __ I N E

4. __ __ __ L Y __ __   9. P H E __ __ __ __ __

5. __ __ __ __ A __   10. __ __ __ G E H __ __ D

Challenge: What country owns Christmas Island?

95

Talk Show

Example: w <u>o</u> R <u>s</u> h I P   t H <u>a</u> N <u>k</u> F U l

1. C O C _ _ _ I _   6. _ E _ _ E T T _ E
2. _ E A _ _ R T _ Y   7. _ _ _ L E _ A L E
3. B _ _ N _ E _ E D   8. T _ _ N _ _ I P
4. _ _ N E Y D E _ _   9. W _ _ _ A _ H O N
5. _ I _ _ B _ N E   10. F O _ _ _ _ L E

Challenge: If guests talk about a klieg light, is the talk show about medicine, near-death experiences, or movie-making?

Babe Ruth

Example: b <u>a</u> R <u>b</u> e R   t <u>r</u> O <u>u</u> G <u>h</u>

1. A _ _ _ O _   6. B _ _ C _ E _
2. _ _ _ _ S T   7. _ A R _ _ _ C K
3. _ _ _ _ Y   8. C _ _ _ C _
4. _ A I _ C _ _   9. F O _ _ _ _
5. _ _ R _ _ L L   10. _ _ A N _ _ G

Challenge: Who starred as Babe Ruth in the movie *Babe*?

Hot Dog

Example: M <u>o</u> N <u>t</u> h L Y   K I N <u>g</u> <u>d</u> <u>o</u> M

1. B _ _ _   3. _ _ _ U
2. _ _ U R _   4. _ I S _ _ R I C

5. P _ _ _ O   8. C _ O C _ L A _ E

6. I N _ I _ _   9. P A _ _ _ A

7. _ U M _ R _ P   10. _ E R E _ _

Challenge: If you're *hotdogging*, what are you doing?

Round Table

Example: S Q u A d r o n   l U b R I C a t e

1. G _ E Y H _ _ _ _   6. _ A _ G E _ _ _ S

2. _ _ P H A _ _ _   7. V E R I _ _ _ _ _

3. A _ J _ _ _ _ E D   8. C E _ E _ R _ _ _

4. I _ T _ _ _ _ C E   9. M _ A _ _ _ _ L

5. _ _ _ _ I S H E _   10. S C _ _ _ _ _ E L

Challenge: Dorothy Parker, James Thurber, and other literary giants met at a round table in what famous New York hotel?

Crew Neck

Example: c O O K w A r e   D e c k H A n D

1. _ _ _ _ K   6. R _ _ _ O _

2. _ I T _ H _ _   7. N I _ _ _ A M _

3. M I _ _ O _ A V _   8. _ A _ T _ H _ E L

4. _ S _ _ O _   9. _ U _ F _ _

5. H _ _ P E _ _   10. _ O _ _ I T _

Challenge: What 1940s movie star was known as the "sweater girl"?

Mom, Dad

Example: B A L d H E a d   A m m o N I A

1. A _ _ _   6. _ I _ E _

2. _ _ D E _   7. _ _ F F O _ I L

3. _ A _ B _   8. C O _ _ A N D _

4. C _ _ _ A   9. S Y _ P T _ _

5. _ E C _ _ E   10. _ _ N _ E L I O N

Challenge: The word *parents* has four anagrams. How many can you find?

Soul Mate

Example: A B s o l u T E   a N t e R O O m

1. H I _ A R I _ _ _   6. D _ _ I _ _ S S E

2. C A R _ _ _ E _   7. N I G H _ _ _ R _

3. H _ _ R G _ A S _   8. M _ _ K M E _ _ N

4. D _ _ D R _ M _   9. G H _ _ _ I _ H

5. B _ S _ _ E N _   10. B _ R O _ _ _ E R

Challenge: In Greek myth, who was the sculpted soul mate of Pygmalion, brought to life by Aphrodite?

Onion Field

Example: W i l d L I f e   S n o o Z i n G

1. _ _ _ C K _ R E _   3. _ P I _ _ _ _ A T E D

2. M _ _ _ S H _ _ E   4. _ _ _ _ G U A R _

5. _ R O _ _ C K _ _

6. C _ M M U _ _ _ _

7. Q U A _ I _ _ _ _

8. C _ _ T _ _ U _ U S

9. _ _ _ T _ X _ C

10. C _ M P A _ _ _ _

Challenge: Who is the author of the novel *The Onion Field*, based on a true event, made into a film?

Zig, Zag

Example: g a R B A N z O   E N E R g i z E

1. _ _ _ M O

2. O O _ _ N _

3. M A _ _ _ I N E

4. _ _ _ E B O

5. _ L _ T _

6. O R _ A N _ _

7. S T _ R _ A _ E R

8. _ O O L O _ _ S T

9. _ _ _ E L L E

10. C O _ N I _ _ N T

Challenge: Elias Howe invented the sewing machine in what year: 1824, 1846, 1865, or 1887?

Army, Navy

Example: F a r m y A R D   H E a v E n L y

1. _ _ _ O R _

2. _ I L I T _ _ _

3. _ _ R _ I _ G

4. _ _ J O _ I T _

5. _ _ C H O _ _

6. _ N _ _ O _ E

7. S _ _ _ T _

8. _ O L U _ T _ R _

9. P H _ _ _ A C _

10. _ I _ E _ _ R D

Challenge: Where are the U.S. Naval Academy and the U.S. Military Academy located?

Milan, Italy

Example: C O <u>m</u> P l a i n <u>a</u> B i l I t <u>y</u>

1. _ _ U _ _ _
2. _ _ _ _ N _
3. _ _ X _ _ _
4. _ _ _ _ _ Y
5. _ _ P _ C _ _

6. A _ _ _ _ _
7. _ _ B _ R _ N _ H
8. _ O _ O R _ _ _
9. P O _ _ C E _ _ _
10. D _ _ _ _ G H _

Challenge: What is the Italian name for the city of Milan?

Far Out

Example: <u>a</u> I r f A R E A S <u>t o u</u> N D

1. D W _ _ _
2. _ _ _ P I A
3. _ _ F _
4. _ _ B _ I C
5. D _ _ B _

6. B _ R R I _ _
7. S T _ _ _ I S H
8. M _ _ S E _ R A P
9. E _ _ _ U L
10. _ _ G B _ A T

Challenge: What "far out" Beat Generation poet authored the landmark poem "Howl"?

Shin Bone

Example: A <u>s</u> T O <u>n</u> i S <u>h</u> <u>b</u> <u>o</u> O K <u>e</u> <u>n</u> D

1. _ A _ D W _ C _
2. _ _ X T E E _ T _
3. D _ _ _ _ A I R

4. A _ D _ M _ _
5. R E _ _ L L I _ _
6. H O M _ _ _ U _ D

7. C _ R _ _ T E _   9. CU _ _ _ O _ ED

8. W _ R K _ _ _ ECH   10. _ Y P _ O T _ _ T

Challenge: What is the scientific name for the shin bone?

Fish Soup

Example: s<u>o</u> A p S <u>u</u> D S   <u>h</u> O U <u>s</u> E W <u>if</u> E

1. _ L O U R _ _ _   6. _ _ O P L _ _ T

2. H _ M E _ _ _ N   7. _ _ R _ T _ A N D

3. _ C _ L _ T _ R   8. C _ _ R T _ H I _

4. _ _ R E _ O U _ E   9. _ _ A C I _ _ S

5. A _ T _ _ _ Y   10. _ _ I S O N O _ _

Challenge: What is the name of the popular French fish soup made in Provence?

Toy Box

Example: A U <u>t</u> H <u>o</u> R I T <u>y</u>   <u>b o</u> R D E A U <u>x</u>

1. A T _ _ R N E _   6. B _ D _ S U I _

2. G E _ M E _ R _   7. E _ H I _ I T _ R

3. _ _ _ L O O D   8. M A _ R I M _ N _

4. _ _ P H _ O N   9. T E _ T _ _ O K

5. L A V A _ _ R _   10. O _ N O _ I _ U S

Challenge: From these anagrams, find "toy box" classics: STEAKS, BROAD MAGES, BLAMERS.

Fast Food

Example: f A N T a s t I C   D R I f T W o o d

1. W _ _ _ E _ U L   6. P R _ _ _ E _
2. _ _ I N T E _ _   7. B E E _ _ _ E _ K
3. _ I R E W _ _ _   8. C _ M _ _ R T E _
4. M _ _ _ E R _ U L   9. C _ N _ _ U N _ E R
5. _ _ N _ A _ I Z E   10. _ L _ _ _ G A T E

Challenge: The anagram LONGED CHASER represents the symbol of what fast food chain?

• Answers •

Word Structure

"X" Marks the Spot

1. buxom
2. Fix-It
3. moxie
4. boxer (Joe Louis)
5. Texas
6. pixie
7. dioxide
8. Quixote
9. inexact
10. proxies
11. prexies, Marxists
12. nonexpert
13. peroxides
14. obnoxious
15. faxes
16. maxim
17. mix-up

Split Ends

1. presto
2. laxest
3. aboard
4. notice
5. chorale
6. bureau
7. baleen
8. lament
9. opined
10. poverty
11. thorny
12. flowery
13. upland
14. frugal
15. timider
16. filial
17. cheapo
18. funded
19. fabric
20. gundog
21. chide
22. dryad
23. among
24. hyena
25. ovate
26. turbo
27. cacti
28. abate
29. welsh
30. afire

Split Ends II

1. greedy
2. bravery
3. widest
4. neuron
5. awoken
6. equated
7. awhirl
8. renown
9. change
10. nonuse
11. disbar
12. croquet
13. evilly
14. limpid
15. oration
16. tragic
17. please
18. unopen
19. finial
20. wintery
21. apart
22. emote
23. leggy
24. ivied
25. mirky
26. hadst
27. apish
28. djinn
29. moldy
30. veldt

Split Ends III

1. apron
2. known
3. ovary
4. exist
5. adieu
6. whipt
7. amuse
8. milky
9. globe
10. twist
11. ajuga
12. awash
13. eking
14. burnt
15. gnawn
16. rinse
17. theme
18. flaxy
19. aging
20. acute
21. chosen
22. yeasty
23. lacrosse
24. chesty
25. climax
26. lattice
27. educate
28. bleary
29. windiest
30. cranky

Split Ends Plus

1. shiest
2. skiddoo
3. sexpot
4. fogless
5. scrawl
6. stalkier
7. slobbery
8. braless
9. screwy
10. stingless
11. scribe
12. scampi
13. sparest
14. smarty
15. sexiness
16. sheath
17. shiver
18. stardom
19. jauntier
20. sharpy
21. ethyl
22. safari
23. playa
24. snipe
25. salient
26. scumming
27. flamingo
28. scowl
29. checkless
30. achiness

Expansion Joint

1. bodices
2. imperial
3. rotund
4. falsie
5. monody
6. gentile
7. cornmeal
8. monkeyed
9. habitant
10. hideouts
11. imprudent
12. bedside
13. playday
14. curious
15. belated
16. mousse
17. turnkey
18. excerpt
19. gonad
20. mortality
21. baluster
22. cowshed
23. waterbed
24. expiration
25. depreciate
26. contingent
27. nutriment
28. insolvent
29. antitrust
30. freshmen

Whodunit

1. J nonparty
2. N trueblue
3. H jaundice
4. P weevilly
5. E earplugs
6. G harbours
7. L schmooze
8. O unafraid
9. I maharaja
10. D crossway
11. F ghettoed
12. A barstool
13. K printout
14. B boroughs
15. Q whodunit
16. C caravans
17. M shrewish

Whodunit II

1. A alphabet
2. Q whizbang
3. O seascape
4. F fiancées
5. G icebergs
6. M reviewer
7. K pinafore
8. D doorjamb
9. I lockjaws
10. B antimale
11. H inhumane
12. L quagmire
13. E episodes
14. J pastrami
15. P wheatear
16. N scrutiny
17. C blastoff

Whodunit III

1. F nondairy
2. K rockabye
3. E minibike
4. Q vagabond
5. J pushcart
6. H pacifist
7. A benefits
8. G nosegays
9. O tomahawk
10. M shellacs
11. C dominoes
12. I peignoir
13. D flyspeck
14. N theorems
15. B crosscut
16. P trusteed
17. L sandwich

Whodunit IV

1. C emblazon
2. E jailbait
3. B disobeys
4. M standoff
5. L sauterne
6. N stargaze
7. A armchair
8. K sapphire
9. P teashops
10. G outblaze
11. O subunits
12. D ensconce
13. Q thespian
14. F monopoly
15. I reattach
16. H plastics
17. J salivary

Whodunit V

1. C barmaids
2. E cochairs
3. H flabbier
4. K halibuts
5. J glaucoma
6. A albacore
7. O residual
8. M plaudits
9. G druggist
10. N ranchero
11. F cousinly
12. Q whiskeys
13. D chaplain
14. L lovelily
15. P sycamore
16. B asterisk
17. I frosteds

eYESight

1. naPOLEon
2. oDOMEter
3. keROSEne
4. bACHElor
5. sHANGhai
6. banKNOTe
7. meRINGue
8. gRAFFiti
9. aPARTheid
10. poINSETtia
11. iTINErary
12. masTERMind
13. uTENsil
14. epSILOn
15. patRIOTic

eYESight II

1. piMIENto
2. heREINto
3. pROSEcute
4. memBRAne
5. arcHANGel
6. proPAGANda
7. cLOVERleaf
8. STILEtto
9. mosQUIto
10. comFORTer
11. impROMPtu
12. afTERMath
13. criTICism
14. aSPARagus
15. alcOHOlic

eYESight III

1. itCHINess
2. orCHESTra
3. marsHALEd
4. dysENTery
5. antiPASTo
6. milLIONth
7. paRAPEts
8. bLOCKade
9. pHARMacy
10. cHAIRman
11. asCRIBes
12. pLATEau
13. ameTHYst
14. bROWNies
15. hoUSEboy

eYESight IV

1. sNOWsuit
2. maCARoni
3. cARMaker
4. doWNbeat
5. impRUDEnt
6. misTHINk
7. nePOTism
8. miNUTest
9. gunFIGht
10. toPOLOgy
11. tiNINEss
12. superHERO
13. cLIENtele
14. taBLEWare
15. unSTABle

Expert eYESight

1. misCONCEption
2. parTICiple
3. thUNDERclap
4. cenTIMEter
5. cANTIlever
6. hoUSEwife
7. conDENSate
8. carboHYDRAte
9. bomBARDier
10. aPOSTrophe
11. proLIFErate
12. maTHEMATICian

Puns & Anagrams

Joyce Shtick—Hospital

1. ambulance: anagram of <u>male Cuban</u>
2. I.C.U.: <u>I see you</u>
3. surgery: <u>Sir</u> + anagram of <u>grey</u>
4. gurney: anagram of <u>un-grey</u>
5. intern: <u>in turn</u>
6. admission: <u>A "D," miss, I only</u>
7. X-ray room: <u>X</u> [after <u>W</u>] + <u>ray</u> + <u>room</u>
8. maternity: anagram of <u>may I rent this</u>
9. emergency: anagram of <u>Gene</u> + <u>mercy</u>
10. insurance: anagram of <u>I can sue, R.N.</u>

Joyce Shtick—Paris

1. Seine: <u>sane</u>
2. Champs-Elysees: anagram of <u>cheesy</u> + <u>samples</u>
3. Orly: anagram of <u>royally</u> minus <u>lay</u>
4. Louvre: anagram of <u>velour</u>
5. Tuileries: anagram of <u>it</u> + <u>leisure</u>
6. Metro: ti<u>me troub</u>le?
7. Notre Dame: <u>not red, A meander</u>
8. Mona Lisa: anagram of <u>so</u> + <u>animal</u>
9. Napoleon: anagram of <u>noon</u> + <u>leap</u>
10. Versailles: <u>over, sail less</u>
11. Latin Quarter: <u>Quartarius</u> (Latin for "quarter")

Joyce Shtick—High School

1. computer: si<u>tcom put Erica</u>
2. exams: anagram of <u>Maxes</u>
3. gym: <u>Jim</u>
4. algebra: anagram of <u>gradable</u> − D
5. midterm: anagram of <u>trimmed</u>
6. art: <u>Art</u>hur
7. English: anagram of <u>shingle</u>
8. Spanish: wing<u>span is</u> <u>h</u>elpful
9. assignment: anagram of <u>SN</u> + <u>steaming</u>
10. teacher: anagram of <u>cheater</u>
11. senior: <u>"C" in your</u>
12. chemistry: Sa<u>chem is</u> <u>try</u>ing

Joyce Shtick—Visiting the Zoo

1. owlet: anagram of <u>towel</u>
2. parrot: anagram of <u>raptor</u>
3. lemur: agile <u>muralist</u>
4. antelope: <u>aunt elope</u>
5. carnivore: anagram of <u>Veronica</u> + R
6. flamingo: <u>flaming orange?</u>
7. kingsnake: anagram of <u>sneaking</u> + K
8. pheasant: anagram of <u>ten</u> + <u>has</u> + <u>Pa</u>
9. egret: fore<u>leg retains</u>
10. bear: <u>bare</u>
11. caiman: anagram of <u>maniac</u>
12. tortoise: anagram of <u>rootiest</u>
13. forest: Be<u>fore strolling</u>

Joyce Shtick—Joy of Foods

1. rosemary: <u>Rose marry</u>
2. lobster: anagram of <u>bolster</u>
3. sole: <u>soul</u>
4. anchovies: anagram of <u>ha</u> + <u>novices</u>

5. kitchen: anagram of thicken
6. abalone: crab alone
7. liverwurst: deliver worst!
8. meringue: anagram of regimen + u (you)
9. pears: Pairs

10. swordfish: Mary's word, fish
11. hamburger: anagram of bear hug + MR
12. ketchup: catch up
13. artichoke: with art, I choke

Joyce Shtick—A Day at the Office

1. appointment: anagram of Pat + mention + P
2. office: anagram of coiffe
3. system: messy, stemware
4. clinch: cinch + L (50)
5. spreadsheet: anagram of she + predates
6. calendar: practical, end around

7. postage: anagram of gestapo
8. chairmen: anagram of machine + R (are)
9. switch: S + which (witch)
10. document: anagram of counted + M (1,000)
11. write: right

Word Doodles & Alphacryptics

Cooking Class

1. banana split
2. chopped liver
3. scrambled eggs
4. apple turnover
5. prune pudding
6. catsup
7. pheasant under glass
8. pears in port wine
9. leftovers

10. round steak
11. pineapple upside-down cake
12. French bread
13. mixed salad
14. shortbread
15. shrimp cocktail
16. eggs over easy

Songs & Musical Compositions

1. "Stand by Me"
2. "Wind Beneath My Wings"
3. "Unfinished Symphony"
4. "The First Noël"
5. "Tiptoe through the Tulips"

6. "Born in the USA"
7. "Moonlight Sonata"
8. "Bridge over Troubled Waters"
9. "High Hopes"

T.V. Time

1. "Little House on the Prairie"
2. "Cheers"
3. "Wheel of Fortune"
4. "48 Hours"
5. "Upstairs Downstairs"
6. "C.H.I.P.S."
7. "Edge of Night"
8. "Murder, She Wrote"
9. "The Price Is Right"

People

1. Flip Wilson
2. Mae West
3. Shelley Long
4. Tina Turner
5. Tiny Tim
6. John Updike
7. Benny Hill
8. Glenn Close
9. Count Basie

Matinee

1. *West Side Story*
2. *French Connection*
3. *Big Top Pee Wee*
4. *From Here to Eternity*
5. *Stripes*
6. *Lost Weekend*
7. *Willow*
8. *Continental Divide*
9. *High Noon* or *Twelve O'Clock High*

Matinee II

1. *All Quiet on the Western Front*
2. *The Big Sleep*
3. *Dr. Dolittle*
4. *Wholly Moses!*
5. *Gone with the Wind, Lost Horizon, The Vanishing*, etc.
6. *Flowers in the Attic*
7. *Gigi*
8. *Meet Me in St. Louis*
9. *White Heat*

Matinee III

1. *Three Men and a Baby*
2. *The Facts of Life*
3. *Time after Time*
4. *Short Circuit*
5. *Separate Tables*
6. *Fiddler on the Roof*
7. *The Longest Day*
8. *All about Eve*
9. *Sea of Love*

Book Club

1. *The Little Minister*
   James M. Barrie
2. *The Turn of the Screw*
   Henry James
3. *The Last of the Mohicans*
   James Fenimore Cooper
4. *No Exit*
   Jean-Paul Sartre
5. *Catch-22*
   Joseph Heller
6. *An Unfinished Woman*
   Lillian Hellman
7. *Henry IV*
   William Shakespeare
8. *A Stranger in a Strange Land*
   Robert Heinlein
9. *Northwest Passage*
   Kenneth Roberts

Book Club II

1. *Go Tell It on the Mountain*
   James Baldwin
2. *The Thirty-nine Steps*
   John Buchan
3. *Oliver Twist*
   Charles Dickens
4. *Room at the Top*
   John Braine
5. *Lie Down in Darkness*
   William Styron
6. "A Season in Hell"
   Arthur Rimbaud
7. *Things Fall Apart*
   Chinua Achebe
8. *East of Eden*
   John Steinbeck
9. "Essay on Man"
   Alexander Pope

Book Club III

1. *Point Counter Point*
   Aldous Huxley
2. *The Lower Depths*
   Maxim Gorky
3. *Letters from the Underworld*
   Fyodor Dostoevski
4. *The 42nd Parallel*
   John Dos Passos
5. *Middlemarch*
   George Eliot
6. *Twelfth Night*
   William Shakespeare
7. *The Sun Also Rises*
   Ernest Hemingway
8. *Two Women*
   Alberto Moravia
9. *So Big*
   Edna Ferber

Book Club IV

1. *Seventeen*
   Booth Tarkington
2. *Ring Round the Moon*
   Jean Anouilh
3. *Man and Superman*
   George Bernard Shaw
4. *Washington Square*
   Henry James
5. *Much Ado about Nothing*
   William Shakespeare
6. *1984*
   George Orwell
7. *Pale Horse, Pale Rider*
   Katherine Anne Porter
8. *A Month in the Country*
   Ivan Turgenev
9. *Heart of Darkness*
   Joseph Conrad

Alphacryptics

1. nohow   2. fatback, finback   3. skip rope   4. joyless
5. bold-faced lie   6. box camera   7. checkpoint   8. no
smoking   9. round robin   10. smallpox

Alphacryptics II

1. stereotyped   2. day in, day out   3. behind times   4. little
woman   5. mixed blessing   6. light bulb   7. square dance
8. front porch   9. double duty   10. leftover

Word Meaning

Double Identities

1. Billy Crystal   2. Ginger Rogers   3. Gene Wilder   4. Spike
Lee   5. Tom Hanks   6. Pearl Buck   7. Mel Brooks   8. Mickey
Mantle

Double Identities II

1. Johnny Cash   2. Holly Hunter   3. Dean Martin   4. Joey
Bishop   5. Art Carney   6. Wilt Chamberlain   7. Kitty Kelly
8. Grace Slick   9. Fats Domino

Double Identities III

1. Ruby Dee   2. Sally Field   3. Peter Coyote   4. Merle
Haggard   5. Victor Mature   6. Tipper Gore   7. Saul Bellow
8. Benny Goodman   9. Beau Bridges

Equivokes

1. b   2. a   3. b   4. c   5. a   6. b   7. a
8. b   9. b   10. b   11. b   12. a   13. c

Equivokes II

1. a   2. c   3. a   4. c   5. b   6. a   7. b
8. a   9. b   10. a   11. c   12. a   13. b

Trivia Word Search

Ziggurat

1. zeitgeist   2. zwieback   3. zombie   4. zilch   5. zoysia
6. Zeppelin   7. Zurich   8. Ziegfeld   9. zero gravity
10. Zapata   11. zenith   12. zoom lens   13. zephyr
14. zucchini   15. zip code   16. zaftig   17. zinfandel   18. zoot
suit   19. Zen Buddhism   20. Zionism

Ziggurat

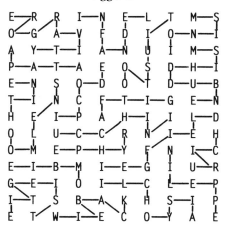

"Y" Knot

1. Yellowstone   2. "YMCA"   3. yellow fever   4. yarrow
5. Yalta   6. William Butler Yeats   7. Yorkshire pudding
8. Yom Kippur   9. "Yankee Doodle"   10. yin and yang
11. yoga   12. yogurt   13. yakitori   14. Yemen   15. Yonkers
16. yearling   17. Yuletide

"Y" Knot

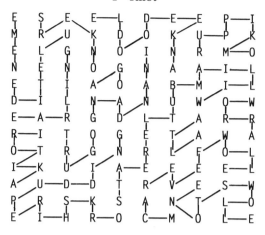

OD'd on "O"

1. Oregon Trail   2. Orpheus   3. Oscar   4. Oberon
5. Outback   6. orchid   7. Olympics   8. olfactory
9. Oedipus   10. Oxford   11. obsolescence   12. Ovid
13. Lee Harvey Oswald   14. Ozarks   15. osculate
16. Oceania   17. Oklahoma   18. Osiris

OD'd on "O"

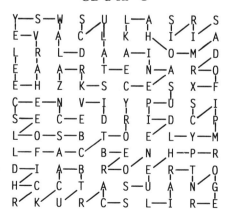

Valedictorian

1. veterinarian   2. vertebrate   3. Vivian   4. Vivaldi
5. vampire   6. vacuum   7. vacation   8. *Vanity Fair*
9. Verona   10. V-E Day   11. Voice of America   12. virtuoso
13. vice squad   14. viper   15. vagrant   16. Vatican
17. *Vertigo*   18. vespers   19. vicarious   20. vegetarian

Valedictorian

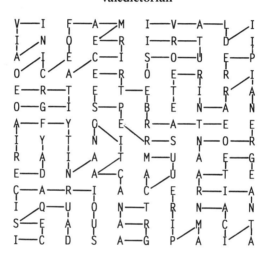

T Square

1. *Twelfth Night*   2. Trafalgar   3. Tasmanian   4. tempera
5. Tripoli   6. tumbrel   7. tempest   8. Teflon   9. teddy bear
10. *Tyrannosaurus*   11. tongue twister   12. Trojan War
13. Tiki   14. triennial   15. testosterone   16. theorem
17. tornado   18. Tierra del Fuego   19. Tory   20. Tonkin

T Square

Relatively Speaking

My Cousin Charley
1. Dialogue and euphoria contain all the vowels: a, e, i, o and u.
2. Munster and Sternum are anagrams.
3. Moby Dick and Jane Eyre each have four letters.
4. Chinos, cello, and ghost contain letters in alphabetical order.
5. Cancan and bonbon contain doubled identical syllables.
6. Adieu and bureau can both be made into plurals with an "x."
7. Pout and gout, complain and pain, rhyme.

Charley's Cats
1. cathedral 2. catamaran 3. muscatels 4. scatology
5. decathlon 6. masticate 7. cataracts 8. medicated
9. suffocate 10. lubricate

Charley's Aunts
1. headhunter 2. orangutan 3. nocturnal 4. paramount
5. sauternes 6. raconteur 7. turntable 8. antifraud
9. flatulent 10. tarantula 11. debutante 12. abduction
13. astronaut 14. suntanned

Charley's Uncles
1. unicycle   2. antiulcer   3. corpulent   4. unbalanced
5. luckiness   6. masculine   7. lunchtime   8. ambulance
9. unethical   10. scoundrel   11. succulent   12. cruelness
13. affluence   14. counselor

Cousinly
1. suspicion   2. incurious   3. seclusion   4. neurotics
5. excursion   6. custodian   7. scouting   8. seduction
9. collusion   10. viscount   11. confusion   12. tenacious
13. carousing   14. inclusion   15. contentious

Aunt Amelia Visits the Zoo
1. zebra   2. wolf   3. hippos   4. otter   5. leopard
6. ocelots   7. raccoon   8. caiman   9. tortoise   10. coyote
Zoologist Level   11. taipan   12. siamangs

Aunt Amelia Visits the Dog Show
1. poodles   2. corgi   3. pointer   4. Irish terrier   5. spaniels
6. Saint Bernard   7. samoyed   8. basset hounds   9. English
setters   10. Labrador

Aunt Amelia Visits the Aviary
1. tern   2. egret   3. heron   4. magpies   5. condor
6. pigeon   7. warbler   8. pelican   9. woodhen   10. moorhen
Ornithologist Level   11. titmouse   12. grosbeak

Aunt Amelia Visits the Aquarium
1. clam   2. oyster   3. tuna   4. shark   5. bluegill   6. sardine
7. lobster   8. blowfish   9. flounder   10. stingray   11. barnacle
12. manatee   13. mussels

Aunt Amelia Visits the Botanic Garden
1. aster   2. daisy   3. sedum   4. salvia   5. lupine   6. crocus
7. petunia   8. oleander   9. geraniums   10. clematis
11. myrtle   **Green Thumb Level**   12. astilbe   13. freesia

Trivia

Litmus Test
1. Uncle Remus   2. Albert Camus   3. Musetta   4. Musketeer
5. mussels   6. mustache   7. Momus   8. shamus   9. musical
10. mushroom   11. Muses   12. Nostradamus

Lit Test
1. lilliputian   2. Bunyanesque   3. Cinderella   4. Judas
5. bacchanal, bacchanalian, or bacchic   6. Tarzan   7. fagin
8. jeremiad   9. jezebel

Trivia Anagrams

What's in a Name?
1. Robert DeNiro
2. Sally Field
3. Adolf Hitler
4. Stevie Wonder
5. Gloria Steinem
6. Oprah Winfrey
7. Steve Martin
8. Clint Eastwood
9. Phil Donahue

What's in a Name II?
1. Norman Mailer
2. Edgar Allan Poe
3. Ernest Hemingway
4. Sir Arthur Conan Doyle
5. Emily Dickinson
6. Henry David Thoreau
7. Tennessee Williams
8. Agatha Christie
9. Edith Wharton

Global Power
1. Peru   2. Iran   3. Niger   4. Burma   5. Libya   6. Italy
7. Crete   8. Spain   9. Yemen   10. Israel   11. Persia
12. Angola   13. Algeria   14. Iceland   15. Palestine
Bonus   1. Bolivia   2. Brazil   3. Chad   4. Chile   5. Congo
6. Cyprus   7. Guinea   8. Holland   9. Japan   10. Jordan
11. Kashmir   12. Morocco   13. Panama   14. Turkey
15. Wales   16. Zaire

Global Power II
1. Las Vegas, Nevada, U.S.A.
2. Darwin, Australia
3. Tunis, Tunisia
4. Venice, Italy
5. Lagos, Nigeria
6. Detroit, Michigan, U.S.A.
7. Athens, Greece
8. Valencia, Spain, or Valencia, Venezuela
9. Seoul, South Korea
10. Leeds, England
11. San Diego, California, U.S.A.
12. Nassau, Bahamas
13. Tucson, Arizona, U.S.A.
14. Caracas, Venezuela
15. Los Angeles, California, U.S.A.

Global Power III
1. madras (Madras, India)
2. bath, also baht (Bath, England)
3. toledo, also looted, tooled (Toledo, Ohio, U.S.A.; Toledo, Spain)
4. buffalo (Buffalo, New York, U.S.A.)
5. paris, also pairs (Paris, France)
6. warsaw (Warsaw, Poland)
7. providence (Providence, Rhode Island, U.S.A.)
8. phoenix (Phoenix, Arizona, U.S.A.)
9. manila, also animal, lamina (Manila, Philippines)
10. hamburg (Hamburg, Germany)
11. bordeaux (Bordeaux, France)
12. victoria (Victoria, Hong Kong; Victoria, British Columbia, Canada)

Anagrams

Symbolically Speaking
1. period, provide
2. colon, colony
3. plus, pulse
4. asterisk, mistakers
5. bracket, backrest
6. plus, slurp
7. colon, uncool
8. comma, hammock
9. bracket, backbiter
10. colon, volcano
11. plus, juleps

Want Adz from A to Z
1. knifed   2. gremlin   3. yogurt   4. wagered   5. varlet
6. esthete   7. misdeed   8. liberal   9. battle   10. xis
11. outspend   12. zoned   13. penalty   14. rampant
15. smokier   16. dimple   17. armrest   18. unnamed
19. nodule   20. fitness   21. hepcats   22. tragedy
23. coupons   24. jitter   25. intones   26. querier

Want Adz II, Short List
1. flatiron   2. misspelt   3. organist   4. boneless   5. virginal
6. crumpets   7. avarice   8. untimely   9. truelove
10. regiment   11. quartile   12. dominoes   13. euphoric
14. gardenia   15. sidestep   16. parried   17. heretics
18. wormiest   19. insisted   20. littered   21. yatter   22. niceness

Want Adz III, Short List
1. murderer   2 aerosol   3. bogeyman   4. coutures
5. vitamins   6. quartets   7. poloist   8. opposer   9. nepotism
10. weirdoes   11. yardmen   12. garnish   13. depletes
14. ultimate   15. infringe   16. trendier   17. lopsided
18. emotions   19. happiest   20. refunded   21. fiendish
22. sunlight

Dog Catcher
1. girlhood   2. devouring   3. knowledge   4. groundhog
5. downgrade   6. wrongdoer   7. dragonfly   8. exploding
9. vagabond   10. shadowing   11. goldenrod   12. congested
13. radiology   14. bandwagon   15. mortgaged   16. obligated
17. guidebook   18. undergone   19. orangeade   20. hydrogen
21. headlong   22. marigold   23. diagnosis   24. prodigies

Manhunt
1. abdominal   2. imaginary   3. macaroni   4. lamebrain
5. malignant   6. dynamite   7. impatient   8. flamingo
9. important   10. gramophone   11. spearmint   12. emotional
13. benchmark   14. abnormal   15. sacrament   16. cinematic
17. dominance   18. geranium   19. machinery   20. rainstorm
21. menopause   22. magnetic   23. comedian   24. enumerate

Category Puzzles

Joint Custody
1. window   2. house   3. sand   4. money   5. square   6. bush or Bush   7. pipe   8. buster or Buster   9. fool's   10. blind

Joint Custody II
1. bull   2. cat   3. dog   4. bug   5. birth   6. cut
7. four or 4-   8. fox   9. ice   10. Northern or northern

Joint Custody III
1. shell   2. spring   3. pig or Pig   4. love   5. hope or Hope
6. glass or Glass   7. electric   8. potato   9. United   10. smoking

Joint Custody IV
1. thumb   2. frost or Frost   3. Western or western   4. flying
5. ginger   6. English   7. spoon   8. counter   9. French or french   10. time or Time

Joint Custody V
1. horse   2. face   3. second   4. show   5. inner   6. Turkish
7. bat   8. Court or court   9. free   10. kid or Kid

Common Denominator
Things That Are Green: grass, money, Kermit
Woody Allen Movies: Bananas, Manhattan, Sleeper
Brushes: paint, tooth, toilet bowl
Islands: Canary, Society, Virgin
Cakes: cheese, coffee, wedding

Common Denominator II
Moores: Demi, Dudley, Mary Tyler
Martins: Dean, Mary, Steve
Woodys: Allen, Guthrie, Woodpecker
Barrymores: Drew, Ethel, Lionel
Stars Who Use One Name: Cher, Madonna, and Prince

Common Denominator III
Stones: Rolling, gall, Flint or flint
Root Plants: ginger, peanuts, sarsaparilla
1960s Dances: pony, jerk, mashed potato
Poets: Frost, Burns, Browning
Things Found in a Car Trunk: dead body, jack, flare

Common Denominator IV
"Yellow   : sunflower, coward, fever
Famous Beaches: Miami, Omaha, Ipanema
Women's Names in Beatles Song Titles: Julia, Rita, Michelle
Things You Pick: cotton, guitar, nose
Things You Catch: cold, train, fish

Common Denominator V
Brontë Sisters: Emily, Anne, Charlotte
Apostles: John, Thomas, Simon
Steaks: chuck, round, flank
Famous Blind People: Oedipus Rex, Ray Charles, Helen Keller
Famous George/Georges: Balanchine, Harrison, Pompidou

Common Denominator VI
Things That Go Up: elevator, blood pressure, zipper
Types of Licenses: marriage, dog, poetic
Things You Blow: kiss, nose, bubble
Types of Mail: junk, air, registered
Grands: Canyon, piano, slam

Letter Patterns

Angelic Devilry
1. jangle   2. general   3. lovebird   4. glance   5. dissolve
6. divulged   7. lasagne   8. vandalize   9. avoidable
10. halogen   11. levied, veiled   12. gasoline   13. drivel
14. lineage   15. evildoer   16. finagled   17. genial   18. gnarliest

Guys & Gals

1. guilty   2. flagpole   3. bodyguard   4. tangelo   5. singular
6. burgundy   7. synagogue   8. young   9. hangnail
10. laughter   11. gauzy   12. sugary   13. yogurt   14. ladybug
15. elegant   16. neurology   17. hooligan   18. gurney

Twofers

Award Night 1. awkwardly 2. hungriest 3. lengthier
4. whistling 5. boardwalk 6. hindsight 7. washboard
8. arrowhead 9. afterward 10. gunfight   **Challenge:** Clio

Coca-Cola 1. alcoholic 2. bachelor 3. illogical 4. stockcar
5. cockroach 6. washcloth 7. democracy 8. scorecard
9. crosswalk 10. coatrack   **Challenge:** nut and leaf

Moby Dick 1. tomboy 2. backside 3. duckling 4. homebody
5. handpick 6. hymnbook 7. sidekick 8. bickered
9. symbolic 10. wickedly   **Challenge:** "Call me Ishmael."

Santa Claus 1. stanza 2. against 3. musical 4. analyst
5. casual 6. nostalgia 7. upscale 8. masculine 9. pheasant
10. stagehand   **Challenge:** Australia

Talk Show 1. cocktail 2. seaworthy 3. blanketed
4. honeydews 5. wishbone 6. teakettle 7. wholesale
8. township 9. walkathon 10. folktale
Challenge: movie-making

Babe Ruth 1. author 2. thrust 3. abbey 4. haircut 5. barbell
6. butcher 7. bareback 8. crutch 9. fourth 10. beanbag
Challenge: John Goodman

Hot Dog 1. both 2. gourd 3. thou 4. historic 5. photo
6. indigo 7. gumdrop 8. chocolate 9. pagoda 10. hereto
Challenge: performing in a showy manner, especially in surfing
or skiing

Round Table 1. greyhound 2. alphabet 3. adjourned
4. introduce 5. nourished 6. dangerous 7. veritable
8. celebrate 9. meatball 10. scoundrel
Challenge: Algonquin Hotel

Crew Neck 1. wreck 2. kitchen 3. microwave 4. escrow
5. henpeck 6. reckon 7. nickname 8. cartwheel 9. curfew
10. cowrite **Challenge:** Lana Turner

Mom, Dad 1. ammo 2. modem 3. mambo 4. comma
5. decade 6. aided 7. daffodil 8. commando 9. symptom
10. dandelion **Challenge:** entraps, pastern, arpents, trepans

Soul Mate 1. hilarious 2. carousel 3. hourglass 4. doldrums
5. basement 6. demitasse 7. nightmare 8. muskmelon
9. ghoulish 10. barometer **Challenge:** Galatea

Onion Field 1. flickered 2. moonshine 3. opinionated
4. lifeguard 5. frolicked 6. communion 7. qualified
8. continuous 9. nontoxic 10. companion
Challenge: Joseph Wambaugh

Zig, Zag 1. gizmo 2. oozing 3. magazine 4. gazebo 5. glitz
6. organza 7. stargazer 8. zoologist 9. gazelle 10. cognizant
Challenge: 1846

Army, Navy 1. armory 2. military 3. varying 4. majority
5. anchovy 6. anymore 7. smarty 8. voluntary 9. pharmacy
10. vineyard **Challenge:** Annapolis, Maryland, and West Point,
New York, respectively

124

Milan, Italy 1. alumni 2. litany 3. laxity 4. mainly
5. typical 6. animal 7. labyrinth 8. monorail 9. policeman
10. daylight   **Challenge:** Milano

Far Out 1. dwarf 2. utopia 3. tofu 4. fabric 5. doubt
6. burrito 7. starfish 8. mousetrap 9. earful 10. tugboat
Challenge: Allen Ginsberg

Shin Bone 1. sandwich 2. sixteenth 3. debonair 4. abdomen
5. rebellion 6. homebound 7. christen 8. workbench
9. cushioned 10. hypnotist   **Challenge:** tibia

Fish Soup 1. flourish 2. homespun 3. sculptor 4. firehouse
5. autopsy 6. shoplift 7. firsthand 8. courtship 9. spacious
10. poisonous   **Challenge:** bouillabaisse

Toy Box 1. attorney 2. geometry 3. oxblood 4. typhoon
5. lavatory 6. bodysuit 7. exhibitor 8. matrimony
9. textbook 10. obnoxious   **Challenge:** skates, board games,
marbles

Fast Food 1. wasteful 2. faintest 3. firewood 4. masterful
5. fantasize 6. proofed 7. beefsteak 8. comforted
9. confounder 10. floodgate   **Challenge:** golden arches
(McDonald's symbol)

• Index •

Answer pages are in italics.

127

About the Authors

Rita Norr was the 1987 National Scrabble® Champion (the first woman ever to hold the title), the 1993 and 1994 Long Island Scrabble® Champion, listed in the *Guinness Book of World Records*, and a member of the U.S. team for the 1993 World Scrabble® championship. She has a B.S. in computer science. She is married, has three children and a golden retriever named Max, and lives in Connecticut.

Audrey Tumbarello is an expert-ranked Scrabble® player, who has worked as a school curriculum developer. She has a degree in American literature and is currently a P.T.A. activist in Brooklyn, New York. She is married and has four children.